NATIONAL GEOGRAPHIC
SCIENCE

D1315716

NATIONAL GEOGRAPHIC

School Publishing

PROGRAM AUTHORS

Randy Bell, Ph.D.

Malcolm B. Butler, Ph.D.

Kathy Cabe Trundle, Ph.D.

Judith S. Lederman, Ph.D.

David W. Moore, Ph.D.

Contents

© NGSP & HB

Contents

© NGSP & HB

Contents

Earth Science, continued

Physical Science

© NGSP & HB

Contents

Science at Home

Dear Family,

In this *Life Science* unit, your child is learning about plants, animals, and their environment. Please use this page to discuss how plants and animals are classified, how they live in their environment, how their parts and behaviors help them survive, and how they change with the seasons.

Big Ideas ....

Your child is learning these important ideas:

- Most plants have leaves that make food, stems that hold up the leaves, and roots that take in water and nutrients and anchor the plant in the soil. Plants respond to heat, gravity, and light. Scientists classify plants according to how they reproduce. Most plants make seeds with flowers or cones. Mosses and ferns make spores.

- The vertebrates (animals with backbones) include fishes, amphibians, reptiles, birds, and mammals. The invertebrates (animals without backbones) include insects, shrimp, corals, spiders, earthworms, and many others. Most animals reproduce by laying eggs. However, most mammals give birth to live young.

- Land and water environments are home to different communities of living things. Community members form food chains. Plants get their energy from the sun. Consumers eat the producers. Decomposers break down dead living things.

- All plants and animals have adaptations, which are features that help them survive in their environment. Examples of adaptations include body parts for protection, getting food, support and movement, controlling temperature, and reproduction. An animal's instincts, or inborn behaviors, are also adaptations.

- Changing with the seasons can help plants and animals survive or avoid cold winters. Examples include trees that shed leaves in the fall; animals that hibernate, or sleep deeply, through the winter; and animals that migrate to warm places.

Share and Learn ....

With your child, make a poster about a plant or animal that lives in your neighborhood. Observe the plant or animal and record your observations. Carefully draw the plant or animal, and then add labels or captions to identify it, describe how it survives in its environment, and how it changes with the seasons.

1

© NGSP & HB

家庭科学教育

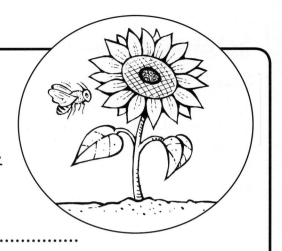

亲爱的家长:

在*生命科学*这一单元中, 您的孩子将了解动植物及其环境。请按照本页所提供的方法, 来与您的孩子共同讨论动植物的分类、在环境中的生存方式、它们利于生存的各部分和习性, 以及随季节的变化。

概念 ....

您的孩子将学到以下这些重要的概念:

- 很多植物都靠叶子产生养分, 植物的茎可支撑叶子, 植物的根可从土壤中吸取水分和养料, 并使植物固定在土壤中。植物对热、地心引力和光都可作出反应。科学家按照植物的繁殖方式对其进行分类。多数植物通过开花获得种子, 或者长出球果作为种子。蕨类及苔藓植物通过孢子进行繁殖。

- 脊椎动物 (有脊椎的动物) 包括鱼类、两栖动物、爬行动物、鸟类和哺乳动物。无脊椎动物 (没有脊椎的动物), 包括昆虫、虾、珊瑚、蜘蛛、蚯蚓等等。许多动物通过生蛋来繁殖。但是也有很多动物直接繁殖后代。

- 陆地和水源是不同生物群落的繁衍场所。不同群落成员构成了食物链。植物从太阳光获得能量。消费者以生产者为食。分解者可以分解死去的生物。

- 所有动植物都具有适应性, 帮助它们在环境中生存。适应性的例子包括各个生命器官, 有的起保护作用, 有的用来获取食物、进行支撑和移动, 有的可控制温度, 有的可进行繁殖。动物的本能 (或天生习性) 也是适应性。

- 动植物随季节变化而变化, 能够帮助它们渡过或躲避寒冷的冬季。这样的例子有: 树木在秋天落叶, 有的动物在冬天冬眠或深度睡眠, 有的动物在冬天要迁徙到温暖地方。

分享和学习 ....

和您的孩子一起制作一张有关附近生长的动植物的海报。观察里面的植物和动物, 然后记下观察到的现象。认真画出动植物, 然后添加标签或文字说明以进行识别, 描述其在环境中的生存方式以及随季节的变化。

© NGSP & HB

Syans Lakay

Bonjou Fanmi,

Nan inite *Syans Lavi* sa a, pitit ou ap aprann enfòmasyon sou plant, bèt, ak anviwònman yo. Tanpri sèvi ak paj sa a pou n diskite klasman plant ak bèt, kijan yo viv nan anviwònman yo, kijan rezon yo ak konpòtman yo ede yo siviv, epi kijan yo chanje lè sezon yo chanje.

Enfòmasyon enpòtan

Men ki enfòmasyon enpòtan pitit ou ap aprann:

- Pifò nan plant yo gen fèy ki fè manje, tij ki kenbe fèy yo, epi rasin ki pran dlo ak nitrisyon epi ki kenbe plant lan nan latè a. Plant bezwen chofaj, gravity ak limyè. Moun lasyans klase plant yo dapre kijan yo repwodyi. Pifò nan plant yo fè grenn ak flè epi pen. Mous ak foujè fè espò.

- Vètebre yo (bèt ki gen kolòn vètebral) se pwason, anfibyen, reptil, zwazo, epi mamifè. Envètebre yo (bèt ki pa gen kolòn vètebral) se ensèk, ekrevis, koray, arenyen, vètè ak anpil lòt ankò. Pifò nan yo repwodyi lè yo ponn ze. Sepandan, pifò nan bèt yo fè tibebe bèt ki tou vivan.

- Anviwònman latè ak dlo fòme kay pou diferan kominote èt vivan. Manm kominote a fòme chenn alimantasyon. Plant jwenn enèji yo bezwen nan solèy la. Konsomatè manje pwodiktè yo. Dekonpozitè yo dekonpoze èt vivan ki mouri.

- Tout plant ak bèt gen adaptasyon, ki la pou ede yo siviv nan anviwònman yo. Egzanp diferan adaptasyon se kote nan kò a pou pwoteksyon, jwenn maje, sipò ak mouvman, kontwole tanperati, epi repwodiksyon. Ensten bèt yo, oubyen konpòtman nòmal yo, se adaptasyon yo ye.

- Chanjman avèk sezon ede plant ak bèt yo siviv oswa evite livè frèt. Egzanp nan sa yo se pyebwa ki pèdi fèy nan òtòn; bèt ki fè ibènasyon, oubyen ki dòmi di, pou livè a; epi bèt ki migre kote ki gen chalè.

Pataje epi Aprann

Ak pitit ou, fè yon afich sou yon plant oubyen yon bèt ki rete nan katye lakay ou. Fè obsèvasyon plant oswa bèt la epi make obsèvasyon ou yo. Byen desinen plant ak bèt la, epi apre mete etikèt oubyen enfòmasyon pou idantifye l, epi dekri kijan li siviv nan aviwònman li, epi kijan li chanje avèk sezon yo.

3

© NGSP & HB

집에서 하는 과학 공부

부모님께,
이번 *생명 과학* 단원에서는 생명체와 생명체가 살고 있는
환경에 대해 배웁니다. 이 페이지를 통하여 동식물을
분류하는 방법과 동식물이 주어진 환경에서 살아가는 방법,
그리고 이들의 몸체 부위와 습성이 생존에 미치는 영향과
계절에 따라 변화하는 방식에 대해 자녀들과 이야기를
나누어 보세요.

개념

자녀는 다음과 같은 중요 개념을 배웁니다.

- 대부분의 식물은 영양분을 만드는 잎과, 잎을 지탱해주는 줄기, 그리고 물과 영양소를
  흡수하며 땅에 식물을 고정시켜주는 뿌리를 가지고 있습니다. 식물은 열과 중력, 그리고
  빛에 반응합니다. 과학자들은 번식 방법에 따라 식물을 분류합니다. 대부분의 식물은
  꽃이나 원뿔 모양의 열매로 씨앗을 만듭니다. 이끼와 양치 식물류는 포자를 만듭니다.

- 척추동물(척추가 있는 동물)에는 어류, 양서류, 파충류, 조류, 그리고 포유류가 있습니다.
  무척추동물(척추를 가지고 있지 않은 동물)에는 곤충, 새우, 산호, 거미, 지렁이, 그 외
  여러 가지 동물이 포함됩니다. 대부분의 동물은 알을 낳아 번식합니다. 그러나 대부분의
  포유류는 새끼를 낳아 번식합니다.

- 육지와 물속 환경은 다양한 생명체의 삶의 터전입니다. 이러한 환경 속에서 구성원들은
  먹이 사슬을 형성합니다. 식물은 태양으로부터 에너지를 얻습니다. 소비자는 생산자를
  먹고 삽니다. 분해자는 죽은 생명체를 분해합니다.

- 모든 식물과 동물은 적응을 통해 자신의 환경에서 생존해 나갑니다. 적응의 예로는 몸체
  부위의 보호 기능, 먹이 습득 기능, 지탱 및 이동 기능, 온도 조절 기능, 그리고 번식 기능
  등이 있습니다. 동물의 본능, 즉 선천적 습성 역시 적응의 한 예입니다.

- 계절에 따른 동식물의 변화는 동식물이 추운 겨울을 견뎌내거나 추위를 피할 수 있도록
  해줍니다. 계절에 따라 변화하는 동식물의 예로는 가을에 잎이 지는 나무, 동면을 하거나
  겨울잠을 자는 동물, 따뜻한 곳으로 이동하는 동물 등이 있습니다.

함께하며 배워요

자녀와 함께 집 근처에 살고 있는 동식물에 대한 포스터를 만들어 보세요.
우선 식물이나 동물을 관찰한 후, 관찰 내용을 기록하세요. 식물이나 동물을 세밀하게
그린 후 해당 동식물의 이름과 어떻게 주어진 환경에서 살아가고 있는지, 그리고 계절에
따라 어떻게 변화하는지 꼬리표나 설명을 덧붙여 달아 보세요.

Имя: _____ Дата: _____

Учимся дома

Уважаемые родители!

Из этого раздела курса *Наука о жизни* ваш ребенок узнает о растениях, животных и среде их обитания. Ознакомившись с информацией на этой странице, вы сможете побеседовать со своим ребенком о классификации растений и животных, об их жизни в природе, о том, как их органы и особенности поведения помогают им выжить, и о том, как живые организмы меняются со сменой времен года.

Это надо знать ···

Ребенок сможет понять и усвоить следующие тезисы.

- У большинства растений есть листья, в которых образуются питательные вещества, стебли, поддерживающие листья, и корни, при помощи которых растения потребляют воду и питательные вещества и закрепляются в почве. Растения реагируют на тепло, силу тяжести и свет. Ученые классифицируют растения в зависимости от способа размножения. Семена большинства растений содержатся в цветах или шишках. Мхи и папоротники размножаются с помощью спор.

- К позвоночным (животным, имеющим спинной хребет) относятся рыбы, земноводные, рептилии, птицы и млекопитающие. К беспозвоночным (животным, не имеющим спинного хребта) относятся насекомые, креветки, кораллы, пауки, дождевые черви и многие другие. Большинство животных размножается, откладывая яйца. Однако у большинства млекопитающих рождаются детеныши.

- Суша и водная среда служат домом для различных сообществ живых организмов. Члены этих сообществ составляют пищевые цепи. Растения получают энергию от солнца. Консументы поедают продуцентов. Редуценты разлагают остатки умерших организмов.

- Все растения и животные обладают механизмами адаптации — свойствами, которые помогают им выжить в среде обитания. К примерам таких механизмов можно отнести части тела, служащие для защиты, добывания пищи, опоры и движения, контроля температуры и размножения. Инстинкты животных, или врожденные поведенческие реакции, также являются разновидностью адаптации.

- Растения и животные меняются со сменой времен года — это помогает им выжить и уберечься от холодов. В качестве примеров можно привести деревья, которые сбрасывают листья осенью, животных, впадающих в спячку на всю зиму, и животных, мигрирующих в теплые края.

Учимся вместе ···

Вместе со своим ребенком создайте плакат, изображающий растение или животное, типичное для вашей местности. Понаблюдайте за этим растением или животным и запишите свои наблюдения. Тщательно нарисуйте выбранное растение или животное и подпишите его название. Опишите, как оно выживает в окружающей среде и как меняется со сменой времен года.

© NGSP & HB

Las ciencias en casa

Estimada Familia,
En este capítulo de *Biología*, su hijo/a aprende sobre las plantas, animales y su ambiente. Utilicen esta página para discutir de qué manera se clasifican las plantas y los animales, cómo viven en su ambiente, cómo sus partes y comportamientos les ayudan a sobrevivir y de qué forma cambian con las estaciones.

Ideas principales

Su hijo/a está aprendiendo estas importantes ideas:

- La mayoría de plantas tienen hojas que producen alimento, tallos que sostienen las hojas y las raíces que llevan el agua y los nutrientes y que fijan la planta al suelo. Las plantas responden al calor, gravedad y luz. Los científicos clasifican las plantas según la forma en que se reproducen. La mayoría de plantas producen semillas con las flores o piñas. Los musgos y los helechos producen esporas.

- Los vertebrados (animales con columna vertebral) incluyen a los peces, los anfibios, los reptiles, las aves y los mamíferos. Los invertebrados (animales sin columna vertebral) incluyen los insectos, los camarones, los corales, las arañas, las lombrices y muchos otros. La mayoría de animales se reproducen poniendo huevos. Sin embargo, la mayoría de mamíferos dan a luz a crías vivas.

- Los ambientes terrestres y acuáticos son el hogar de diferentes comunidades de seres vivos. Los miembros de la comunidad forman cadenas alimentarias. Las plantas obtienen su energía del sol. Los consumidores se comen a los productores. Los descomponedores desintegran los seres que han muerto.

- Todas las plantas y los animales tienen adaptaciones que les ayudan a sobrevivir en su ambiente. Entre los ejemplos de adaptaciones están las partes del cuerpo que utilizan para protegerse, obtener alimentos, apoyarse y moverse, controlar la temperatura y reproducirse. Los instintos de un animal, o comportamientos innatos, también son adaptaciones.

- Los cambios según las estaciones pueden ayudar a las plantas y a los animales a sobrevivir o evitar el clima frío del invierno. Entre los ejemplos están los árboles que mudan sus hojas en el otoño; los animales que hibernan, es decir, que duermen profundamente durante el invierno; y los animales que migran a lugares cálidos.

Compartir y aprender

Con su hijo/a, haga un cartel sobre una planta o un animal que viva en su vecindario. Observen la planta o al animal y anoten sus observaciones. Dibujen cuidadosamente la planta o el animal, y luego agreguen etiquetas o leyendas para identificarlo, describir cómo sobrevive en su ambiente y cómo cambia con las estaciones.

6

© NGSP & HB

Khoa Học ở Nhà

Thân gửi Quý Phụ Huynh,

Trong bài về *Khoa Học Cuộc Sống* này, con em Quý Vị sẽ học về thực vật, động vật, và môi trường sống của chúng. Vui lòng sử dụng trang này để thảo luận cách phân loại thực vật và động vật, cách chúng tồn tại trong môi trường sống của mình, cách các bộ phận và hành vi của chúng giúp chúng tồn tại, và cách chúng thay đổi theo mùa như thế nào.

Các Khái Niệm Quan Trọng

Con em của Quý Vị sẽ được học về các khái niệm quan trọng sau đây:

- Hầu hết các loại thực vật đều có lá để tạo thức ăn, thân cây giúp giữ lá, còn rễ cây giúp hấp thụ nước, chất dinh dưỡng và giữ chặt cây trong đất. Các loài thực vật phản ứng với nhiệt, trọng lực và ánh sáng. Các nhà khoa học phân loại các loài thực vật theo cách chúng sinh sản như thế nào. Hầu hết các loài thực vật đều tạo ra hạt trong hoa hoặc quả. Các loại rêu và dương xỉ tạo ra bào tử.

- Các loài có xương sống (là các loài động vật có cột sống) gồm có các loài cá, động vật lưỡng cư, bò sát, chim, và động vật có vú. Các loài không có xương sống (là các loại động vật không có cột sống) bao gồm sâu bọ côn trùng, tôm, san hô, nhện, giun đất, và nhiều loại động vật khác. Hầu hết các loài động vật đều đẻ trứng. Tuy nhiên, hầu hết các loài động vật có vú lại sanh con.

- Môi trường đất và nước là nhà của các cộng đồng sinh vật khác nhau. Các thành viên trong cộng đồng hình thành nên các dây chuyền thức ăn. Thực vật tiếp thu năng lượng từ mặt trời. Các loài sinh vật dị dưỡng ăn các loài sinh vật tự dưỡng. Các sinh vật phân hủy phân giải các sinh vật chết.

- Tất cả các loài thực vật và động vật đều có đặc điểm thích nghi giúp chúng tồn tại trong môi trường sống của mình. Các ví dụ về đặc điểm thích nghi gồm có các bộ phận cơ thể giúp bảo vệ, lấy thức ăn, hỗ trợ và di chuyển, kiểm soát nhiệt độ, và sinh sản. Bản năng của động vật, hoặc hành vi bẩm sinh, cũng là đặc điểm thích nghi.

- Thay đổi theo mùa có thể giúp cho các loài động vật và thực vật sống sót hoặc tránh được thời tiết mùa đông lạnh giá. Các ví dụ gồm có cây rụng lá vào mùa thu; động vật ngủ đông, hoặc ngủ rất sâu trong suốt mùa đông; và một loài động vật di trú đến những vùng có khí hậu ấm áp.

Chia Sẻ và Học Tập

Cùng các em, tạo một bức tranh về thực vật hoặc động vật sống trong vùng của quý vị. Hãy quan sát các loại động vật hoặc thực vật và ghi lại những gì đã quan sát được. Vẽ cẩn thận các loài thực vật hoặc động vật, sau đó dán nhãn hoặc chú thích để nhận biết chúng, miêu tả cách chúng tồn tại trong môi trường sống của mình, và cách chúng thay đổi theo mùa như thế nào.

© NGSP & HB

Explore Activity

Investigate Plants and Gravity

 **How does gravity affect the growth of plant roots?**

Predict

Lay cup A on its side. Do not change the position of cup B. In which direction will the roots of each plant grow? Write your prediction.

_____

_____

_____

_____

Turn cup A upright. Do not change the position of cup B. In which direction will the roots of each plant grow? Write your prediction.

_____

_____

_____

_____

© NGSP & HB

Explore Activity   continued

Record

Write and draw what you observe in the table below.

How Plant Roots Grow

Day	Cup A Observations	Cup B Observations

© NGSP & HB

Explore Activity continued

Explain and Conclude

1. Do the results support your predictions? Use your observations to explain.

_____

_____

_____

_____

_____

2. Infer the way gravity affects the growth of plant roots. Tell what evidence from this activity you observed to make your inference.

_____

_____

_____

_____

_____

© NGSP & HB

Chapter 1 Science Vocabulary

Write one of the vocabulary words in each blank to complete the sentence.

> environment
> germinate
> organism
> pollen
> reproduce
> spore

1. A plant, animal, or other living thing is called a(n) _____.

2. The male parts of a flower make _____.

3. Seeds begin to grow when they _____.

4. All of the living and nonliving things around an organism are its _____.

5. A tiny part of a moss or fern that can grow into a new plant is a(n) _____.

6. Most plants _____ by making flowers, seeds, and fruits.

Write a sentence about this drawing. Use a vocabulary word.

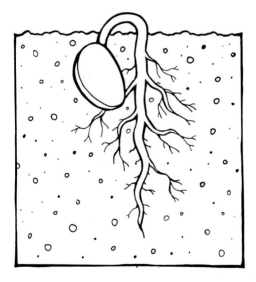

_____

_____

11

© NGSP & HB

Chapter 1 Share and Compare

Draw pictures in each box to show the life cycle of an apple tree.

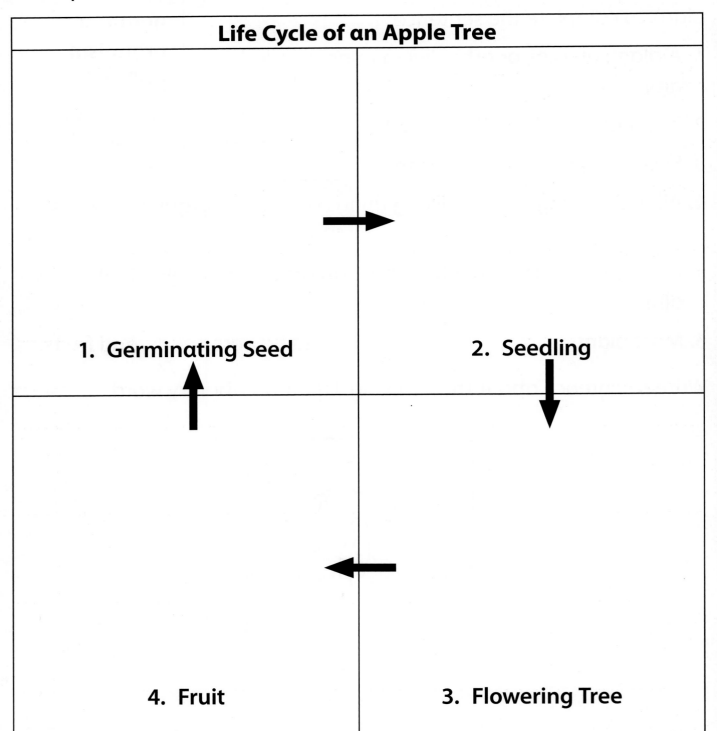

Life Cycle of an Apple Tree

1. Germinating Seed

2. Seedling

4. Fruit

3. Flowering Tree

© NGSP & HB

Directed Inquiry

Investigate Plant Parts

 **How can you classify plants by their parts?**

Record

Write and draw what you observe in the table below.

Observations of Plant Picture Cards

Sunflower	
Rye grass	
Corn	
Boston fern	
Moss	
Bracken fern	

13

© NGSP & HB

Directed Inquiry continued

Write and draw what you observe in the table below.

Observations of Seeds and Spores

Sunflower seed	
Rye grass seed	
Corn seed	
Spore slide	

Classify the plants on Picture Cards 7–9.

Classification of Plants

Plant	Seed-Producer or Spore-Producer?
Echinacea	
Sword fern	
Plumeria	

© NGSP & HB

Directed Inquiry   continued

Explain and Conclude

1. How are the plants on all the Picture Cards similar and different?

_____

_____

_____

_____

_____

2. How did your observations of seeds and spores help you to classify the plants on Picture Cards 7–9?

_____

_____

_____

_____

_____

© NGSP & HB

Directed Inquiry   continued

3. Share your classification with other groups. Talk about other ways that you could classify the plants on the Picture Cards.

_____

_____

_____

_____

_____

Think of Another Question

What else would you like to find out about the parts of plants? How could you find an answer to this new question?

_____

_____

_____

_____

_____

Name _____ Date _____

Investigate Animal Classification

 **Question** How can you identify animals with backbones and model how a backbone works?

Record

Write and draw what you observe in the table below.

Animal Classification

Animal	Observations	Backbone or No Backbone?
Chimpanzee		
Clownfish		
Earthworm		
Horse		
Snake		

© NGSP & HB

Directed Inquiry   continued

Animal Classification continued

Animal	Observations	Backbone or No Backbone?
Squid		
Sea sponge		
Robin		
Lobster		
Snail		

Observe

What did you observe as you bent and twisted your model backbone?
Write your observations below.

_____

_____

_____

© NGSP & HB

Directed Inquiry   continued

Explain and Conclude

1. How did you use your observations to classify the animals as animals with backbones and animals without backbones?

_____

_____

_____

_____

2. Infer how the structure of the backbone helps an animal move different ways. Use your observations of the model backbone to explain your answer.

_____

_____

_____

_____

Directed Inquiry continued

Think of Another Question

What else would you like to find out about animals with backbones and how their backbones work? How could you find an answer to this new question?

_____

_____

_____

_____

_____

© NGSP & HB

Chapter 2 Science Vocabulary

Write one of the vocabulary words in each blank to complete the sentence.

**backbone
classify
invertebrate
vertebrate**

1. The _____ protects the main nerve cord in some animals.

2. Characteristics are used to _____ organisms, or place them in groups.

3. A cheetah is a(n) _____ because it has a backbone.

4. A grasshopper is a(n) _____ because it does not have a backbone.

Classify each of these organisms as a vertebrate or invertebrate.

5. _____

6. _____

7. _____

8. _____

Chapter 2 Extend Learning

Classify Animals by Group

Animal: _____

Choose an animal pictured in the Big Ideas Book. Write its name and draw it. Then answer the questions in the table. Your animal is classified in the group that has the most *yes* answers.

Fish	**Bird**
Does it have a backbone? _____	Does it have a backbone? _____
Does it live in water? _____	Does it have feathers and two legs covered with scales? _____
Does it have fins, scales, and gills? _____	Does it have two wings? _____
Do the young hatch from eggs? _____	Do the young hatch from eggs? _____
Amphibian	**Mammal**
Does it have a backbone? _____	Does it have a backbone? _____
Does it live part of its life in water and part of its life on land? _____	Does it have hair or fur? _____
Does it have four legs and thin, damp skin? _____	Are the young born live? _____
	Does it make milk to feed its young? _____
Do the young hatch from eggs? _____	
Reptile	**Arthropod**
Does it have a backbone? _____	Does it have a hard outside skeleton instead of a backbone? _____
Is it covered in hard scales that are not shiny? _____	Does it have jointed legs? _____
Does it have lungs and breathe air? _____	Is its body divided into sections? _____
Do the young hatch from eggs? _____	Do the young hatch from eggs? _____

© NGSP & HB

Chapter 2 Extend Learning continued

Draw an example of a vertebrate and an invertebrate. Then write one or two sentences that explain how they are different.

Vertebrate	Invertebrate

_____

_____

Chapter 2 Share and Compare

Draw an example of each kind of organism. Then share and compare your examples with a partner.

Arthropod	Fish
Amphibian	Reptile
Bird	Mammal

24

© NGSP & HB

Investigate Fossils

Question How can you classify living things that lived long ago?

Record

Write and draw your observations in the table below.

Fossil

Characteristic	Observations
Length	
Shape	
Other features	

25

© NGSP & HB

Guided Inquiry   continued

Explain and Conclude

1. Was your fossil animal an invertebrate or a vertebrate? What was its environment like? How do you know?

_____

_____

_____

_____

_____

2. How else could you classify the fossils?

_____

_____

_____

_____

_____

Guided Inquiry continued

Think of Another Question

What else would you like to find out about classifying living things that lived long ago? How could you find an answer to this new question?

_____

_____

_____

_____

_____

© NGSP & HB

Guided Inquiry continued

Investigate Fossils

Fossil Information

Fossil	What It Looks Like	What Scientists Know	Vertebrate or Invertebrate?
ammonite		• Shells were usually the only part that became fossils because the soft body was rarely preserved. • Their spiral-shaped shell was hard like today's snail shell. • They probably lived in open ocean water rather than at the bottom. • They ate other animals such as reptiles, softer shelled animals, and other small animals. They grabbed prey with tentacles.	
shark tooth		• Teeth were usually the only part that became fossils because their skeletons were made of cartilage—the same kind of material that makes up your ears and the tip of your nose. • They lived in seas that covered what is now land. • They ate other animals that lived in the water.	
trilobite		• They lived in oceans where they moved over the ocean floor looking for food. They ate other very small animals or living things that had died. • They belonged to the same group of animals as insects and lobsters. • Their outer covering was similar to that of a crab or lobster today. • They had a toothless mouth, but could suck water and prey into their mouths.	

Investigate Fossils

Fossil Information

Fossil	What It Looks Like	What Scientists Know	Vertebrate or Invertebrate?
fish		• Fish fossils are common in many parts of the world. There were many different kinds of fish that left behind fossils. • Many fossil fish resembled fish that live today.	
gastropod		• They belonged to the same group of animals as snails and slugs. • Most fossils are of shells because they had very soft bodies. • The first gastropods lived in oceans. • They ate both plants and tiny animals that floated in water. • Inside the mouth was a feeding structure that was made up of thousands of tiny teeth-like structures that helped shred food.	
crinoid stem		• Made of three sections, a tough stem filled with muscles, the major organs, and the arms. Usually only the stem formed fossils. • They filtered small particles of food from seawater with their feather-like arms. • They looked like plants, but were animals.	

Directed Inquiry

Investigate Interactions in a Model Pond

 **How do living things in a model pond ecosystem interact?**

Record

Write and draw what you observe in the table below.

Model Ecosystem

Model Pond Part	Observations	Living or Nonliving?	What I Infer About Its Needs	Producer or Consumer?
Sand				
Elodea plant				
Rocks				
Water				
Snails				

30

© NGSP & HB

Directed Inquiry continued

Draw your model pond ecosystem. Circle the living things. Draw arrows to show how energy moves from the sun to the producers and consumers in the pond ecosystem.

My Model Pond Ecosystem

Explain and Conclude

1. How did your observations help you classify producers and consumers in your ecosystem?

_____

_____

_____

31

© NGSP & HB

Directed Inquiry   continued

2. How did this model help you understand how living things in a real pond ecosystem interact?

_____

_____

_____

_____

_____

Think of Another Question

What else would you like to find out about how living things interact in a pond ecosystem? How could you find an answer to this new question?

_____

_____

_____

_____

© NGSP & HB

Chapter 3 Science Vocabulary

Write one of the vocabulary words in each blank to complete the sentence.

community
consumer
decomposer
food chain
population
producer

1. All the bison in one area make up a _____.

2. All the living things in the same area form a _____.

3. A grass plant is classified as a _____ because it makes its own food.

4. A wolf is classified as a _____ because it eats other living things for food.

5. An earthworm is a _____ because it breaks down living things that have died.

6. An oak tree, caterpillar, robin, and bobcat form a _____ in which energy passes from one organism to the next.

Label each organism in the diagram as a producer or consumer. Then write a caption to describe the diagram.

_____   _____   _____

_____

_____

Chapter 3 Extend Learning

Classify Animals in Food Chains

Observe each illustration and read the caption. Then enter the names of the 7 animals in both charts on the next page.

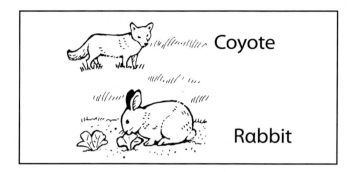

Rabbits eat plants only. Coyotes hunt and eat rabbits and other animals.

Opossums eat many kinds of fruit. They also eat insects, frogs, snakes, and other small animals.

Zebras eat grass. Lions hunt and eat zebras and other grazing animals.

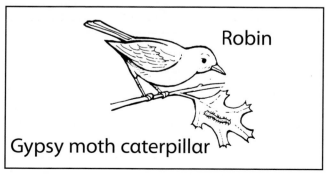

Gypsy moth caterpillars eat leaves. Robins eat worms, insects, and many kinds of fruit.

© NGSP & HB

Chapter 3 Extend Learning continued

Herbivores	Carnivores	Omnivores

Predators	Prey

Write sentences to answer these questions.

1. How are herbivores and carnivores alike? How are they different?

_____

_____

_____

2. How are all the predators alike? How are they different?

_____

_____

3. How could an animal be both predator and prey?

_____

_____

© NGSP & HB

Chapter 3 Share and Compare

In the box, draw the three living things. Connect them with arrows to show a food chain. Label each living thing as a producer or consumer.

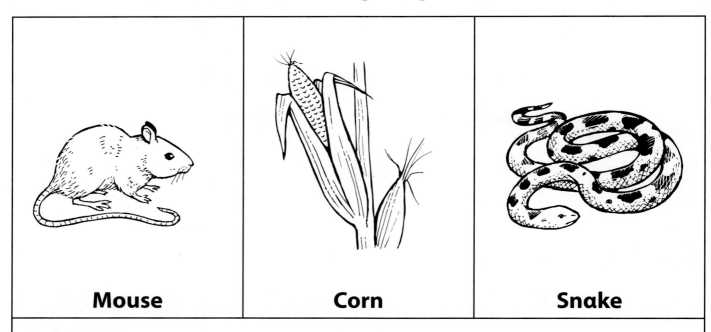

| **Mouse** | **Corn** | **Snake** |

Food chain

© NGSP & HB

Investigate Brine Shrimp

> **Question** How do different amounts of salt in the water affect hatching of brine shrimp eggs?

Make a Hypothesis

How will the amount of salt affect the number of brine shrimp eggs that hatch?

_____

_____

_____

Identify and Control Variables

Which variable will you change?

_____

Which variable will you observe or measure?

_____

Which variables will you keep the same?

_____

_____

Guided Inquiry   continued

Observe

What are your observations of the brine shrimp eggs in step 1?

_____

_____

Record

Write what you observe in the table below.

Estimated Number of Brine Shrimp

	Cup 1: Control (1 ½ Spoonfuls of Salt)	Cup 2: ____ Spoonfuls of Salt	Cup 3: ____ Spoonfuls of Salt
Day 1			
Day 2			
Day 3			
Day 4			

© NGSP & HB

Guided Inquiry   continued

Explain and Conclude

1. Compare the number of brine shrimp that hatched in each cup.

_____

_____

_____

_____

_____

2. What can you conclude about how different amounts of salt affect the hatching of brine shrimp eggs?

_____

_____

_____

_____

_____

© NGSP & HB

my SCIENCE notebook

Guided Inquiry continued

Think of Another Question

What else would you like to find out about how different amounts of salt affect brine shrimp? How could you find an answer to this new question?

_____

_____

_____

_____

_____

© NGSP & HB

Investigate Plant Adaptations

Question How does a leaf's covering affect how quickly it wilts?

Record

Write and draw what you observe in the table below.

Comparing Leaves

Day and Time	Observations of Leaf With Waxy Coating	Observations of Leaf Without Waxy Coating
Start		

© NGSP & HB

Directed Inquiry continued

Predict

Which leaf will wilt more quickly in sunlight? Write your prediction.

_____

_____

_____

_____

Explain and Conclude

1. Do the results support your prediction? Explain.

_____

_____

_____

_____

_____

42

© NGSP & HB

Directed Inquiry   continued

2. Share your results with others. Did they get the same results? Explain any differences.

_____

_____

_____

_____

_____

3. Infer which kind of leaf covering is more likely to be found on plants that live in a dry place.

_____

_____

_____

_____

_____

© NGSP & HB

Directed Inquiry continued

Think of Another Question

What else would you like to find out how a plant's covering affects wilting? How could you find an answer to this new question?

_____

_____

_____

_____

_____

44
© NGSP & HB

Chapter 4 Science Vocabulary

adaptation	camouflage	instinct	mimicry

Write one of the vocabulary words in each blank to complete the sentence.

1. A mother fox has a(n) _____ to find a den and protect her young.

2. The tail end of a caterpillar looks like a snake. This shows _____.

3. The sharp claws and teeth of a grizzly bear are each a(n) _____ for getting food.

4. A chameleon has _____ because it blends in with its background.

Define the word **adaptation**. Use the cactus as an example.

_____

_____

_____

_____

_____

Chapter 4 Share and Compare

Complete each sentence to show how plants and animals adapt to survive. Use the words and phrases in the box.

channels
broad leaves
tongues
food
pollinators
stems
blubber
thorns

Plants	**Animals**
Rain forest plants have _____ to take in sunlight.	Grizzly bears have sharp claws to grasp _____ .
Cacti have thick _____ for storing water.	Chameleons use long, sticky _____ to catch insects.
Blackberry bushes have _____ for protection.	Seals have _____ that helps control body temperature.
Nectar is an adaptation to attract _____ .	Thorny lizards have _____ that collect water.

46
© NGSP & HB

 **Math in Science**

Graphing Data

What Did You Find Out?

1. Why do scientists use different kinds of graphs to organize data?

_____

_____

_____

_____

_____

2. Which kind of graph would you use to show how the height of a seedling changes over a month? Why?

_____

_____

_____

_____

 continued

Graph Data

Seeds and Flowers

Flower	Number of Seeds
1	100
2	400
3	800
4	500

1. Make a pictograph of the data. Write a title at the top. Make a row for each flower.
2. Decide what symbol you will use and how many seeds one symbol will stand for. Make a key.
3. Draw the correct number of symbols in each row.

© NGSP & HB

Guided Inquiry

Investigate Temperature and Coverings

Question   How does a covering affect the temperature when a thermometer is placed in very cold water?

Make a Hypothesis

How will the covering affect the temperature of the thermometer?

_____

_____

_____

Identify and Control Variables

Which variable will you change?

_____

Which variable will you observe or measure?

_____

Which variables will you keep the same?

_____

_____

_____

© NGSP & HB

Guided Inquiry continued

Predict

What will happen to the temperature of each thermometer?

_____

_____

Record

Write what you observe in the table below. Record which type of material you used to cover the thermometer.

Temperature Change in Thermometers

Time	Temperature of Thermometer without Covering	Temperature of Thermometer Covered with _____
Start		
1 minute		
2 minutes		
3 minutes		
4 minutes		
5 minutes		
6 minutes		
7 minutes		
8 minutes		
9 minutes		
10 minutes		

Guided Inquiry   continued

Explain and Conclude

1. Compare the temperatures of the two thermometers. Was your hypothesis supported? Explain.

_____

_____

_____

_____

_____

2. Share your results with other groups. What type of covering kept the thermometers the warmest?

_____

_____

_____

_____

_____

© NGSP & HB

Guided Inquiry · continued

3. Use the results of your experiment to infer how body coverings help animals live in cold temperatures.

_____

_____

_____

_____

_____

Think of Another Question

What else would you like to find out about how coverings affect temperature? How could you find an answer to this new question?

_____

_____

_____

_____

© NGSP & HB

Investigate Temperature and Cricket Behavior

Question **How does temperature affect cricket behavior?**

Predict

How will the cooler temperature affect the crickets' behavior?

_____

_____

Record

Write your observations in the table below.

Cricket Activity

Where Habitat Was	Temperature (°C)	Observations
Classroom		
Refrigerator (after 10 minutes)		
Room temperature (after 5 minutes)		

my SCIENCE notebook

Directed Inquiry   continued

Explain and Conclude

1. Share your results with the class. Did your results support your predictions? Explain.

_____

_____

_____

_____

_____

2. How did the change in temperature affect the crickets' behavior?

_____

_____

_____

_____

© NGSP & HB

Directed Inquiry   continued

3. When the temperature of its environment gets cooler, the processes in a cricket's body slow down. Infer how this might affect a cricket's ability to move and survive.

_____

_____

_____

_____

_____

Think of Another Question

What else would you like to find out about how temperature affects crickets' behavior? How can you find an answer to this new question?

_____

_____

_____

_____

Directed Inquiry continued

Stages in the Life of a Cricket

An adult cricket can survive the warm summer months in many parts of the United States. But in fall, cooler temperatures cause processes in the cricket's body to slow down. In the cold winter temperatures, the adult cricket dies.

A cricket egg, however, can survive the colder temperatures of winter. In the warmer months of spring, a young cricket emerges from the egg. The young cricket grows through the summer to become an adult. In fall, the adult cricket lays eggs. The eggs will hatch the following spring.

Cut out the four stages of the cricket life. Use the information above to help you place them in order. Start with summer. Circle the stage in which crickets survive the cold temperatures of winter.

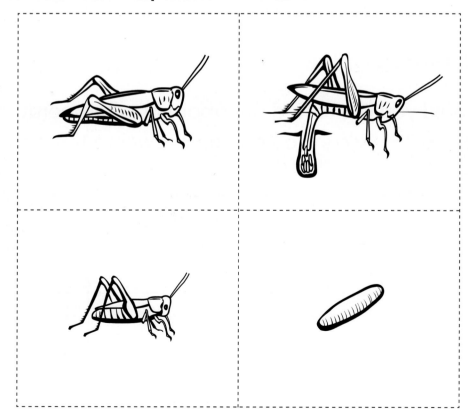

Chapter 5 Science Vocabulary

Write one of the vocabulary words in each blank
to complete the sentence.

**deciduous
evergreen
hibernate
migrate
season**

1. A chipmunk will _____ , or sleep deeply,
   during the winter.

2. A pine tree is a(n) _____ because it keeps
   its leaves during the year.

3. Many geese _____ to warm places in the fall.

4. A(n) _____ is a time of year with certain patterns
   of weather.

5. A maple tree is _____ because it sheds its leaves in
   the fall.

Write a caption and add labels to the drawing. Use vocabulary words.

_____

_____

my SCIENCE notebook

Chapter 5 Share and Compare

Complete each sentence to show how plants and animals respond to cold winters. Use the words and phrases in the box.

> change color
> grow thick coats
> hibernate
> keep leaves
> migrate
> shed leaves
> store food in bulbs

Plants	Animals
Deciduous trees _____.	Musk oxen _____.
Evergreens _____.	Arctic foxes _____.
Lillies, daffodils, and onions _____.	Chipmunks _____.
	Monarch butterflies _____.

© NGSP & HB

Name _____   Date _____

Investigate Temperature and Seed Sprouting

 **How does temperature affect seed sprouting?**

Make a Hypothesis

How will the temperature affect seed sprouting? Write your hypothesis.

_____

_____

_____

Identify, Manipulate, and Control Variables

Which variable will you change?

_____

Which variable will you observe or measure?

_____

Which variables will you keep the same?

_____

Guided Inquiry   continued

Record

Write and draw what you observe in the table below.

Temperature and Seed Sprouting

Day	Observations	
	Bag 1: _____ °C	Bag 2: _____ °C
Start: After 30 minutes		
1		
3		
5		

Guided Inquiry   continued

Explain and Conclude

1. Which seed had grown more by the end of the week?

_____

_____

_____

_____

_____

2. What can you conclude about temperature and how seeds sprout?

_____

_____

_____

_____

_____

© NGSP & HB

Guided Inquiry   continued

3. How might seed growth be affected in places that have cold winters?

_____

_____

_____

_____

_____

Think of Another Question

What else would you like to find out about temperature and seed sprouting? How could you find an answer to this new question?

_____

_____

_____

_____

_____

© NGSP & HB

Open Inquiry

Do Your Own Investigation

Open Inquiry Checklist

❑ Choose a question or make up one of your own.

_____

_____

❑ Gather the materials you will use.

_____

_____

_____

_____

_____

❑ If needed, make a hypothesis or a prediction.

_____

_____

_____

_____

Name _____ Date _____

Open Inquiry continued

❏ If needed, identify, manipulate, and control variables.

_____

_____

_____

_____

❏ Make a plan for your investigation.

_____

_____

_____

_____

_____

_____

_____

_____

© NGSP & HB

Open Inquiry continued

❏ Carry out your plan.

❏ Collect and record data. Analyze your data.

Open Inquiry   continued

❑ Explain and share your results.

_____

_____

_____

_____

❑ Tell what you conclude.

_____

_____

_____

❑ Think of another question.

_____

_____

_____

Open Inquiry

SAMPLE QUESTION AND STEPS

Investigate Plants and Light

Question How do light and darkness affect how seeds sprout and grow?

Materials				
2 cups with soil	tape	6 sunflower seeds	spoon	cup with water

What to Do

1 Label 1 cup with soil **Light.** Label the other cup with soil **Dark.**

What to Do, continued

2 **Observe** the sunflower seeds. Then use the spoon to plant 3 seeds in each cup. Make sure to cover the seeds with soil.

3 Use the spoon to water the seeds. Give each cup 2 spoonfuls of water each day.

4 Put the Light cup in a sunny place. Put the Dark cup in a dark place with a similar temperature as the Light cup. Observe your cups each day for 2 weeks, and record your observations.

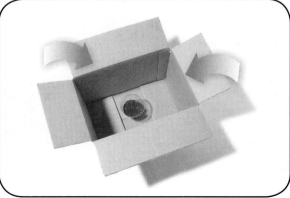

Name _____   Date _____

 **Think** Like a Scientist

How Scientists Work

Using Models to Study Systems

What Did You Find Out?

1. What is a system?

_____

_____

_____

_____

2. What are three kinds of models scientists might use to study an ecosystem?

_____

_____

_____

_____

 continued

Plan a Model

1. What question are you trying to answer?

_____

_____

_____

_____

_____

2. What kind of model or models would you use?

_____

_____

_____

_____

_____

© NGSP & HB

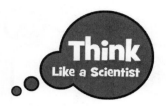 continued

3. Write a procedure for using the model to answer the question.

_____

_____

_____

_____

4. After talking with others, what changes might you make to your plan?

_____

_____

_____

_____

© NGSP & HB

Science at Home

Dear Family,
In this *Earth Science* unit, your child is learning about the sun and other stars, the moon, Earth, resources on Earth, how Earth's surface changes, and weather. Please use this page to talk with your child about the sun, stars, moon, and Earth.

Big Ideas ....

Your child is learning these important ideas:

- Earth orbits around the sun. Earth rotates on its axis, causing day and night. The moon is a satellite of Earth and appears to move across the sky from east to west.

- The sun is a star that appears large and bright because it is close to Earth. It emits energy. Energy from the sun is important for life on Earth.

- A star is a glowing ball of hot gases. Stars vary in size and brightness. Stars also vary in color depending on their temperature.

- Rocks have different properties, such as color, layering, and texture. Soil is made of bits of rock, air, and humus. Soil has different properties, such as color, texture, and how it can hold water and support plant growth.

- Some of Earth's resources are renewable and some are nonrenewable. People must care for Earth's resources so they don't run out.

- Weathering breaks down or wears away rock. Erosion carries small pieces from one place to another. These slow changes shape Earth's landforms.

- Earthquakes, volcanoes, landslides, and weather events can change Earth's surface quickly. These changes may be harmful to living things.

- As water moves through the water cycle, it can change to a solid, a liquid, or a gas. Earth's supply of water is recycled as it moves through the water cycle.

Share and Learn ....

With your child, take a walk on a sunny day. Observe and discuss the difference in the warmth you feel as you walk in the sunlight and then in the shade. Talk about what might happen if energy from the sun ever stopped. If you live in an area where urban lights don't block out the stars, observe the night sky with your child. See if you can distinguish brighter stars from dimmer stars and stars of different colors.

家庭科学教育

亲爱的家长:

在地球科学这一单元中, 您的孩子将了解太阳及其他恒星、月亮、地球、地球上的资源、地表变化和天气。请按照本页所提供的方法, 来与您的孩子共同讨论太阳、恒星、月亮和地球。

概念 ....

您的孩子将学到以下这些重要的概念:

- 地球围绕太阳旋转。地球绕地轴进行自转, 便有了白天和黑夜。月亮是地球的卫星, 看起来是从东向西在天空中移动。

- 太阳是恒星, 因为太阳距离地球很近, 所以看起来又大又亮。太阳会发出能量。太阳能对地球上的生物非常重要。

- 恒星是热气构成的一个发光发热的球体。然而恒星的大小和亮度各不相同。温度不同, 恒星的颜色也不同。

- 岩石具有多种特性, 例如颜色、结构和成分。土壤由少量的岩石、空气和腐殖质组成。土壤具有多种特性, 例如颜色、成分以及是否能保持水源并支持植物生长。

- 有些地球资源是可再生的, 有些是不可再生的。人类必须保护地球资源, 防止资源用尽。

- 岩石经风化会分解或侵蚀。侵蚀会移动碎片。缓慢地改变地球地形。

- 地震、火山、山体滑坡和天气事件能够迅速改变地球表面。这些变化对生物来说可能有害。

- 水在循环过程中, 可以变成固态、液态或气态。在水的循环过程中, 地球实现了供水的再循环。

分享和学习 ....

和您的孩子一起在阳光明媚的天气散步。观察并讨论走在阳光里和走在阴影中感受到的温度差异。讨论如果太阳不散发能量的话, 将会发生什么情况。如果您居住的地方夜景不会受到城市灯光的干扰, 那么带上您的孩子一起观察夜空。看是否能够区分恒星的明暗以及颜色不同的恒星。

© NGSP & HB

Syans Lakay

Bonjou Fanmi,

Nan seksyon *Syans Latè* sa a, pitit ou ap aprann sou solèy ak lòt zetwal yo, lalin lan, Latè a, resous sou Latè a, kijan sifas Latè a chanje, epi lameteyo. Tanpri, sèvi ak paj sa a pou w eksplike pitit ou kisa solèy, zetwal, lalin ak Latè ye.

Enfòmasyon enpòtan

Men ki enfòmasyon enpòtan pitit ou ap aprann:

- Latè a nan òbit toutotou solèy la. Latè a vire sou aks li, ki fè gen jou ak nyit. Lalin lan se yon satelit Latè a epi li parèt pou l bouje nan syèl la de ès a lwès.

- Se yon zetwal solèy la ye men li parèt gwo epi klere poutèt se pre li pre Latè a. Li pwodyi enèji. Enèji solèy la enpòtan anpil pou Latè a.

- Yon zetwal se yon boul ki gen gaz cho kap briye. Zetwal yo varye nan dimansyon ak briyans yo. Zetwal yo varye tou nan koulè yo tou depannde tanperati yo.

- Wòch gen pwopriyete diferan, tankou koulè, kouch ak teksti. Nan tè gen ti moso wòch, van, ak imis. Tè gen diferan pwopriyete, tankou koulè, teksti, epi kijan li ka kenbe dlo epi sipòte plant k ap pouse.

- Gen nan resous Latè a ki ka renouvle epi gen lòt ki pa ka renouvle. Se pou moun fè atansyon ak resous Latè a pou yo pa fini.

- Chanjman nan lameteyo kase epi dekonpoze wòch yo. Ewozyon pote ale ti moso depi yon kote ale yon lòt. Chanjman dousman sa yo fòme tè Latè a.

- Tranblemanntè, vòlkan, glisman teren, ak lameteyo ka chanje sifas Latè a vit. Chanjman sa yo ka danjre pou ètvivan.

- Lè dlo deplase nan sik dlo a, li ka chanje pou l vin yon solid, yon likid, oubyen yon gaz. Pwovizyon dlo sou Latè a resikle lè l deplase nan sik dlo a.

Pataje epi Aprann

Al fè lamach avèk pitit ou, yon jou ki gen solèy. Obsève epi diskite sou diferans sou chalè ou santi a lè w mache anba limyè solèy la ak lè w mache nan lonbraj. Pale sou sa ki ka rive si enèji ki soti nan solèy la janm kanpe. Si w abite nan yon zòn kote limyè ibèn yo pa bloke zetwal yo, obsève syèl la lanwit avèk pitit ou. Gade pou wè si w ka distenge zetwal ki pi briyan yo ak zetwal ki mwen briyan yo ak zetwal ki gen koulè diferan yo.

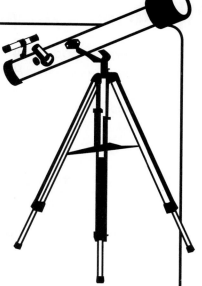

집에서 하는 과학 공부

부모님께,
이번 *지구 과학* 단원에서는 태양 및 다른 항성(별), 달, 지구, 지구의 자원,
지구의 표면 변화 및 날씨에 대해 배웁니다. 이 페이지를 통하여 태양,
항성, 달 및 지구에 대해 자녀와 이야기를 나누어 보세요.

개념

자녀는 다음과 같은 중요 개념을 배웁니다.

- 지구는 태양의 궤도를 공전합니다. 낮과 밤은 지구가 지축을 중심으로
  자전하면서 생깁니다. 달은 지구의 위성이며 동쪽 하늘에서 서쪽
  하늘로 이동하는 것처럼 보입니다.

- 태양은 항성이고 지구 가까이에 있기 때문에 매우 크고 밝게 보입니다.
  태양은 에너지를 발산합니다. 이렇게 발산된 에너지는 지구의 생명체에 중요한
  역할을 합니다.

- 항성은 뜨거운 기체로 이루어진 빛나는 덩어리입니다. 항성은 크기와 밝기가 모두
  각기 다릅니다. 또한 항성의 온도에 따라 나타나는 색깔도 각기 다릅니다.

- 암석은 색, 층 및 질감 등 각기 다른 특성을 지닙니다. 토양은 바위 부스러기, 공기와
  부식토로 만들어집니다. 토양은 색과 질감을 비롯하여 수분을 함유하고 식물의
  성장을 돕는 방식과 같은 특성이 서로 다릅니다.

- 지구의 자원은 재생이 가능한 자원과 재생이 불가능한 자원으로 구성되어 있습니다.
  사람들은 지구의 자원이 고갈되지 않도록 소중히 사용해야 합니다.

- 풍화 작용은 바위를 잘게 부수거나 닳게 합니다. 침식 작용은 작은 물질을 이동시키는
  역할을 합니다. 지구의 지형은 이와 같이 느린 변화들을 통해 조금씩 변경됩니다.

- 지진, 화산 활동, 산사태 및 기상 현상은 지구의 표면을 빠르게 변화시킬 수 있습니다.
  하지만 이와 같은 급격한 변화는 생명체에 위협을 줄 수 있습니다.

- 물은 순환 과정을 통해 이동하면서 고체, 액체 또는 기체로 변화합니다. 이러한 순환
  과정을 통해 물은 재활용됩니다.

함께하며 배워요

자녀와 함께 맑은 날 산책을 해 보세요. 햇빛 속을 걸을 때와 그늘에서 걸을 때 느끼는
따뜻함의 차이를 관찰하고 토론해 봅니다. 태양 에너지가 지구에 도달하지 못할 경우
어떤 일이 생길지 이야기해 보세요. 도시의 불빛이 별빛을 가리지 않는 지역에 산다면
자녀와 함께 밤하늘을 관찰해 보세요. 밝은 별과 어두운 별, 그리고 색깔이 다른 별을
구분할 수 있는지 파악합니다.

Учимся дома

Уважаемые родители!

При изучении раздела *Наука о Земле* ребенок узнает о Солнце и других звездах, Луне, Земле, ресурсах Земли, процессах изменения земной поверхности и погоде. Материал на этой странице поможет вам организовать с ребенком беседу о Солнце, звездах, Луне и Земле.

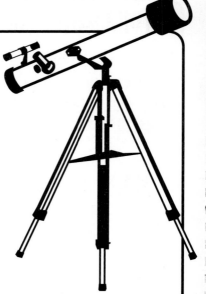

Это надо знать ....

Ребенок сможет понять и усвоить следующие тезисы:

- Земля вращается вокруг солнца. Земля вращается вокруг своей оси, что приводит к смене дня и ночи. Луна — это спутник Земли, и мы видим, как она движется по небу с востока на запад.

- Солнце — это звезда, которая кажется нам большой и яркой, потому что расположена близко к Земле. Солнце излучает энергию. Энергия Солнца важна для жизни на Земле.

- Звезда — это светящийся шар, состоящий из горячих газов. Звезды отличаются размером и яркостью. Звезды также бывают разного цвета в зависимости от их температуры.

- Горные породы обладают различными свойствами, такими как цвет, структура и разделение на слои. Почва состоит из мелких частичек горных пород, воздуха и перегноя. Почва различается по таким свойствам, как цвет и структура, а также способность удерживать воду и поддерживать рост растений.

- На Земле есть возобновляемые и невозобновляемые ресурсы. Люди должны бережно относиться к ресурсам Земли, чтобы они не иссякли.

- Под воздействием атмосферных явлений горные породы выветриваются или разрушаются. В процессе разрушения мелкие частички переносятся из одного места в другое. В результате постепенно меняется рельеф земной поверхности.

- Землетрясения, вулканы, оползни и другие погодные явления могут быстро изменять поверхность Земли. Такие изменения могут быть губительны для всего живого.

- По мере того как вода проходит все стадии круговорота воды в природе, она может переходить в твердое, жидкое или газообразное состояние. Благодаря круговороту воды пополняются запасы воды на Земле.

Учимся вместе ....

Совершите прогулку с ребенком в солнечный день. Наблюдайте за разницей в теплоте, которую вы ощущаете, когда находитесь сначала на солнце, а затем в тени, и обсудите эту разницу. Поговорите о том, что могло бы произойти, если бы энергии Солнца не стало. Если вы живете в местности, где огни города не заслоняют звезды, понаблюдайте за ночным небом вместе с ребенком. Посмотрите, сможете ли вы отличить яркие звезды от менее ярких и различать звезды разного цвета.

© NGSP & HB

Las ciencias en casa

Estimada Familia,
En este capítulo de *Ciencias de la Tierra*, su hijo/a aprende acerca del sol y otras estrellas, la luna, la Tierra, recursos de la Tierra, cómo cambia la superficie de la Tierra y el clima. Utilice esta página para hablar con su hijo/a sobre el sol, la luna y la Tierra.

Ideas principales ··

Su hijo/a está aprendiendo estas importantes ideas:

- La Tierra orbita alrededor del sol. La Tierra rota sobre su eje, lo que causa el día y la noche. La luna es un satélite de la Tierra y parece moverse a través del cielo de este a oeste.

- El sol es una estrella que se ve grande y brillante porque está cerca de la Tierra. Emite energía. La energía del sol es importante para la vida en la Tierra.

- Una estrella es una esfera encendida de gases calientes. Las estrellas varían en tamaño y brillo. Las estrellas también varían en color, dependiendo de su temperatura.

- Las rocas tienen diferentes propiedades, como color, textura y capas. El suelo está hecho de pedazos de roca, aire y humus. El suelo tiene diferentes propiedades, como color, textura, almacenamiento de agua y permite el crecimiento de las plantas.

- Algunos de los recursos de la Tierra son renovables y algunos no son renovables. Las personas deben cuidar los recursos de la Tierra para que no se agoten.

- La sedimentación destruye o desgasta las rocas. La erosión lleva pequeñas piezas de un lugar a otro. Estos lentos cambios dan forma a los accidentes geográficos de la Tierra.

- Los terremotos, volcanes, deslizamientos y eventos climáticos pueden cambiar rápidamente la superficie de la Tierra. Estos cambios pueden ser dañinos para los seres vivos.

- A medida que el agua se mueve a través del ciclo de agua, puede cambiar a un sólido, un líquido o un gas. El suministro de agua de la Tierra se recicla a medida que se mueve a través del ciclo de agua.

Compartir y aprender ··

Den un paseo con su hijo/a en un día soleado. Observen y hablen sobre la diferencia del calor que sienten mientras caminan bajo la luz del sol y luego en la sombra. Hablen de lo que podría suceder si la energía del sol alguna vez se interrumpiera. Si viven en un área en donde las luces de la ciudad permiten ver las estrellas, observen el cielo nocturno con su hijo/a. Miren si pueden distinguir las estrellas más brillantes de las que tienen menos brillo y estrellas de diferentes colores.

© NGSP & HB

Khoa Học ở Nhà

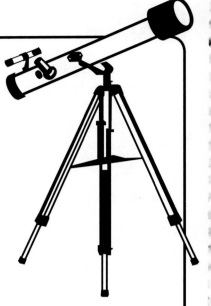

Thân gửi Quý Phụ Huynh,
Trong bài này *Khoa Học Trái Đất*, con em Quý Vị học về mặt trời và các tinh cầu khác, mặt trăng, Trái Đất, nguồn tài nguyên trên Trái Đất, cách thay đổi của bề mặt của Trái Đất, và thời tiết. Xin hãy sử dụng trang này để nói chuyện với các em về mặt trời, các tinh cầu, mặt trăng, và Trái Đất.

Các Khái Niệm Quan Trọng

Con em của Quý Vị được học các khái niệm quan trọng sau đây:

- Trái Đất quay quanh mặt trời. Trái Đất tự xoay quanh trục của nó, tạo ra ngày và đêm. Mặt trăng là một vệ tinh của Trái Đất và di chuyển trên bầu trời từ đông sang tây.

- Mặt trời là một tinh cầu lớn và sáng vì nó gần với Trái Đất. Mặt trời tỏa ra năng lượng. Năng lượng từ mặt trời rất quan trọng đối với cuộc sống trên Trái Đất.

- Một tinh cầu là một quả cầu rực rỡ được cấu thành bởi khí nóng. Các tinh cầu khác nhau có kích thước và độ sáng khác nhau. Màu sắc của các tinh cầu cũng khác nhau tùy thuộc vào nhiệt độ của chúng.

- Đá có các đặc điểm khác nhau, như màu sắc, địa tầng, và kết cấu. Đất được tạo thành từ các mẩu đá, không khí, và đất mùn. Đất có các đặc điểm khác nhau, như màu sắc, kết cấu, và cách nó có thể giữ nước và giúp cây cối phát triển như thế nào.

- Một vài nguồn tài nguyên trên Trái Đất có thể tái tạo được và một vài loại không thể tái tạo được. Con người phải chăm sóc đến nguồn tài nguyên của Trái Đất để chúng không bị cạn kiệt.

- Thời tiết làm đứt gãy hoặc mài mòn đá. Sự xói mòn đem theo các mảnh nhỏ từ nơi này đến nơi khác. Những biến đổi chậm này hình thành nên địa mạo của Trái Đất.

- Động đất, núi lửa, lở đất, và các sự kiện thời tiết có thể làm thay đổi bề mặt của Trái Đất một cách nhanh chóng. Những biến đổi này có thể gây hại đến mọi sinh vật.

- Khi nước chuyển động theo chu trình nước, nó có thể biến đổi thành chất rắn, chất lỏng, hoặc chất khí. Nguồn cung cấp nước cho Trái Đất được phục hồi khi nước chuyển động theo chu trình nước.

Chia Sẻ và Học Tập

Hãy đi dạo trong một ngày nắng đẹp cùng với con em bạn. Hãy quan sát và thảo luận về mức độ nóng khác nhau ta cảm nhận được khi đi dưới ánh nắng mặt trời và khi ở trong bóng râm. Thảo luận về những gì có thể xảy ra nếu như năng lượng từ mặt trời không còn nữa. Hãy quan sát bầu trời đêm cùng với con em bạn nếu nơi bạn sống ánh sáng của các tinh cầu không bị lấn át bởi ánh đèn đô thị. Nhìn xem liệu bạn có thể phân biệt được độ sáng và màu sắc của các tinh cầu khác nhau hay không.

Explore Activity

Investigate Moon Phases

 **How can you model the way the moon's shape seems to change?**

Record

Observe the Calendar of Moon Phases. Is there any pattern to the way the moon looks? Describe the pattern you see.

_____

_____

_____

_____

_____

_____

_____

_____

© NGSP & HB

Explore Activity   continued

Draw how the moon's shape appears to change.

Changes in the Moon's Shape in One Month

© NGSP & HB

Explore Activity   continued

Explain and Conclude

1. What pattern do you see in your model of moon phases?

_____

_____

_____

_____

2. Describe how your model shows the phases of the moon.

_____

_____

_____

_____

81
© NGSP & HB

Explore Activity   continued

3. Suppose you are able to see the whole moon in the night sky. Use your model to predict how the shape of the lighted part of the moon will change over the next week.

_____

_____

_____

_____

_____

© NGSP & HB

Explore Activity   continued

Moon Calendar

Sunday	Monday	Tuesday	Wednesday	Thursday	Friday	Saturday
1	2	3	4	5	6	7
8	9	10	11	12	13	14
15	16	17	18	19	20	21
22	23	24	25	26	27	28

© NGSP & HB

Explore Activity continued

Moon Phase Pictures

Cut out each moon phase picture. Then put the pictures in order.

© NGSP & HB

Explore Activity continued

Moon Phase Pictures continued

© NGSP & HB

Chapter 1 Science Vocabulary

Answer each question using a word from the box.

phase	revolves	rotates	satellite

1. What does Earth do when it travels around the sun?

_____

2. What is the lighted shape of the moon that we see from Earth?

_____

3. What revolves around a planet?

_____

4. What does Earth do when it spins around?

_____

Draw a picture of Earth's orbit. Write the word *orbit* in a sentence.

_____

_____

Chapter 1 Extend Learning

Investigate the Day and Night Cycle

Question Does the day and night cycle change?

Date	Sunrise Time	Sunset Time	Night Sky Observations

1. How different was the sunrise time on the last date from the sunrise time on the first date? _____

2. About how many hours pass between each sunrise? Between each sunset? _____

3. How long is the day and night cycle? _____

4. How did the night sky change over the two weeks?_____

_____

Chapter 1 Share and Compare

Identify the patterns by filling in the blanks. Use the words in the box below.

day	night	phases	year

Half of Earth faces away from the sun.

_____

Half of Earth faces toward the sun.

_____

Patterns

Earth revolves.

_____

The moon revolves.

_____

Draw a picture that shows how Earth and the moon revolve. Include the sun, Earth, and moon in your picture.

Math in Science

Bar Graphs

What Did You Find Out?

1. What kind of data would scientists show on a bar graph?

_____

_____

_____

_____

_____

2. How can you tell what the different bars on a graph stand for?

_____

_____

_____

© NGSP & HB

 continued

Make and Use a Graph

Look at the data below about the rocks in a particular area.
Then use the data to make a bar graph.

Kind of Rock	How Many Collected
Granite	1
Shale	3
Sandstone	5
Pumice	2

Write a title for your graph. Write numbers and **How Many Collected** on the side of the graph. Write **Kind of Rock** and the name of each rock at the bottom. Draw bars to show how many of each rock were collected.

Title: _____

_____ _____ _____ _____

_____

Investigate Sunlight and Shadows

 **How does a shadow caused by sunlight change during the day?**

Record

What are your observations of the toy's shadow in step 1?

_____

_____

_____

_____

Write or draw your observations and measurements in the table below.

Changes in Shadows

Date	Time	How High the Sun Looks	Length of Shadow (cm)

Directed Inquiry continued

Changes in Shadows, continued

Date	Time	How High the Sun Looks	Length of Shadow (cm)

Predict

Where will the toy's shadow be 1 hour after your last observation? Write your prediction.

_____

_____

_____

After 1 hour, does your observation match your prediction? Why or why not?

_____

_____

_____

© NGSP & HB

Directed Inquiry continued

Explain and Conclude

1. Compare your measurements. When was the shadow the shortest and longest? Where was the sun in the sky at those times?

_____

_____

_____

_____

_____

2. What pattern in length and movement did you observe with the shadows?

_____

_____

_____

_____

_____

© NGSP & HB

Directed Inquiry continued

3. What caused the changes you observed in the shadows?

_____

_____

_____

_____

_____

_____

Think of Another Question

What else would you like to find out about sunlight and shadows?
How could you find an answer to this new question?

_____

_____

_____

_____

_____

Directed Inquiry

Investigate Energy from the Sun

 **What happens to the temperature of water when it is in the sunlight and in the shade?**

Record

Write what you observe in the table below.

Water Temperature

Cup	At Start (°C)	After 1 Hour (°C)	After 2 Hours (°C)
Sun		In sunlight	In shade
Shade		In shade	In shade

Directed Inquiry continued

Explain and Conclude

1. Compare the temperatures of the water in the 2 cups at the end of 1 hour in step 4.

_____

_____

_____

_____

_____

2. What happened to the temperature of the water in the Sun cup when it was moved from the sunlight to the shade? Explain why you think this happened.

_____

_____

_____

_____

© NGSP & HB

Directed Inquiry continued

3. Share your data with others. Explain any differences in the data.

_____

_____

_____

_____

_____

Think of Another Question

What else would you like to find out about sunlight and water temperatures? How could you find an answer to this new question?

_____

_____

_____

_____

_____

Chapter 2 Science Vocabulary

Draw a line from the vocabulary word to its meaning.

1. energy

2. transform

3. light

4. temperature

5. sun

a. a kind of energy you can see

b. a measure of how hot or cold something is

c. star nearest to Earth

d. the ability to do work or cause change

e. to change

Circle the word that completes each sentence correctly. Then write the word on the line.

6. The sun is a _____.

    planet   star

7. The sun gives Earth heat and _____.

    light   air

© NGSP & HB

Chapter 2 Share and Compare

Fill in the lines with the letters identifying the information that is true for each kind of energy.

Food energy ____ ____   Solar energy ____ ____

Fossil fuels ____ ____ ____   Wind energy ____ ____

    a. created by plants now

    b. often used to make electricity

    c. made from plants and animals that lived long ago

    d. collected by solar panels

    e. used, directly or indirectly, by animals

    f. coal, gasoline, and natural gas are types

    g. turns windmills

Write a short paragraph about how people depend on energy from the sun.

_____

_____

_____

_____

_____

_____

© NGSP & HB

Guided Inquiry

Investigate Sunlight

 **How well do different materials block sunlight?**

Make a Hypothesis

Which materials will block sunlight from the light-sensitive beads? Write your hypothesis.

_____

_____

_____

Identify, Manipulate, and Control Variables

Which variable will you change?

_____

_____

Which variable will you observe or measure?

_____

Which variables will you keep the same?

_____

_____

© NGSP & HB

Guided Inquiry continued

Record

Write what you observe in the table below.

Light-Sensitive Beads

Location	Material Tested	Observation of Beads (no change, slight change, full change)
Shade		
Sunlight		
Sunlight		
Sunlight		

101

© NGSP & HB

Guided Inquiry   continued

Explain and Conclude

1. Do the results support your hypothesis? Explain.

_____

_____

_____

_____

_____

2. Compare what happened to the beads in steps 1 and 2. What caused the change in step 2?

_____

_____

_____

_____

_____

© NGSP & HB

Guided Inquiry   continued

3. What can you conclude about how well materials block sunlight? What evidence did you use to come to your conclusion?

_____

_____

_____

_____

_____

Think of Another Question

What else would you like to find out about how to block sunlight? How could you find an answer to this new question?

_____

_____

_____

_____

_____

© NGSP & HB

Investigate Light Brightness

Question **How does a light's brightness appear to change with distance?**

Record

Use the Apparent Brightness Scale below to describe brightness.
Write what you predict and observe in the table below.

Apparent Brightness Scale	
1	very bright
2	bright
3	dim

Distance and Apparent Brightness of Lights

	Penlight	Distance from Observer	Predicted Brightness	Observed Brightness
Start	A	2 m		
	B	2 m		
	C	2 m		

© NGSP & HB

Directed Inquiry   continued

Distance and Brightness of Lights, continued

	Penlight	Distance from Observer	Predicted Brightness	Observed Brightness
Trial 1	A	2 m		
	B	4 m		
	C	3 m		
Trial 2	A	2 m		
	B	3 m		
	C	4 m		
Trial 3	A	2 m		
	B	5 m		
	C	4 m		

Directed Inquiry   continued

Explain and Conclude

1. Do your results support your predictions? Explain.

_____

_____

_____

_____

_____

2. What can you conclude about distance and the apparent brightness of lights that are the same size? Use your observations to support your conclusion.

_____

_____

_____

_____

_____

© NGSP & HB

Directed Inquiry continued

3. Use the results of this investigation to explain how stars that are like each other in size and temperature can appear to have different brightnesses.

_____

_____

_____

_____

_____

Think of Another Question

What else would you like to find out about how a light's brightness appears to change with distance? How could you find an answer to this new question?

_____

_____

_____

_____

Chapter 3 Science Vocabulary

Write one of the words from the box to complete each sentence. You can use the words more than once.

star	property	brightness	telescope

1. Something you can observe about an object, such as its size, is a(n) _____ of that object.

2. A(n) _____ is a glowing ball of hot gases that can be seen in the night sky.

3. The amount of light an object gives off is called _____.

4. When you look through a(n) _____, the things that you look at seem closer and bigger.

5. Color is a(n) _____ of stars that gives a clue to how hot they are.

6. A scientist can see more detail by using a(n) _____ to study the stars.

7. The hottest stars have the greatest _____ because they give off the most energy for their size.

8. Choose two words from the box and write a sentence about stars that contains both words.

_____

_____

108

© NGSP & HB

Chapter 3 Share and Compare

Complete each circle of the web with a property of stars. Choose the property from the box that relates best to the words above or below each circle.

brightness	color	size	temperature

dwarfs   giants   shining   glowing

_____   _____

Stars

_____   _____

hotter   cooler   white   yellow

Explain how different properties affect the brightness of stars.

_____

_____

_____

_____

_____

Guided Inquiry

Investigate Lenses

 **Question**   **How can lenses help you see objects that are far away?**

Compare

How large did the words look with each lens in step 1?

_____

_____

_____

_____

_____

Record

What lenses did you choose to make your telescope?

_____

_____

_____

© NGSP & HB

Guided Inquiry   continued

Record

Write what you observe in the table below.

Observing Stars

	Observations
Without telescope	
With telescope	
With telescope reversed	
With another group's telescope	

Guided Inquiry continued

Explain and Conclude

1. How did turning the telescope around affect the stars you observed?

_____

_____

_____

_____

_____

2. Compare the number of stars you could observe with your telescope and without a telescope.

_____

_____

_____

_____

_____

© NGSP & HB

Guided Inquiry continued

3. Use your observations to explain how lenses can help scientists study stars.

_____

_____

_____

_____

_____

Think of Another Question

What else would you like to find out about how lenses can help you see objects that are far away? How could you find an answer to this new question?

_____

_____

_____

_____

Investigate Rock Layers

Question **How can you model and compare rock layers?**

Record

Write or draw in the table below.

Rock Model

Layer	Materials Used	Observations
Bottom		
Middle		
Top		

© NGSP & HB

Directed Inquiry continued

Explain and Conclude

1. Compare the layers of your model.

_____

_____

_____

_____

_____

2. Compare your model rock to those of other students. Why do you think the models look different?

_____

_____

_____

_____

_____

© NGSP & HB

Directed Inquiry continued

3. How is your model rock like the real rocks in the picture on page 111? How is it different?

_____

_____

_____

_____

_____

Think of Another Question

What else would you like to find out about rock layers? How could you find an answer to this new question?

_____

_____

_____

_____

_____

Chapter 4 Science Vocabulary

Answer each question using a word from the box.

grain	humus	mineral	soil

1. What is composed of bits of decayed plants and animals? _____

2. What is a solid, nonliving material found in nature? _____

3. What is the word for a small part of a rock or soil? _____

4. What material from Earth is made up of bits of rocks, decayed matter, air, and water? _____

Draw a picture of two minerals from this chapter.

Write sentences describing the properties of each mineral you drew.

_____

_____

Chapter 4 Extend Learning

Investigate the Ability to Support Plant Growth

Question Which soil type best supports plant growth?

Date	Sandy Soil	Red Clay Soil	Humus Soil

1. How much did the plants grow in the humus soil after five days? How did this compare with the seeds in the red clay and sandy soil?

_____

2. How well do each of the soils hold water? How do you think this affects plant growth?_____

_____

_____

_____

© NGSP & HB

Chapter 4 Share and Compare

Examine the Venn diagram. Answer the questions below it.

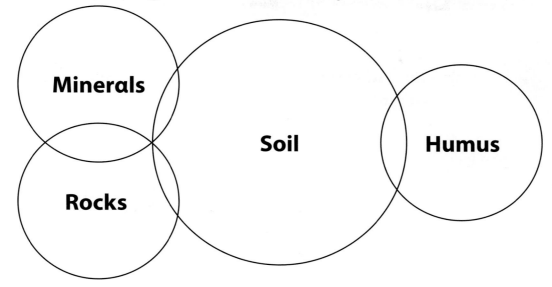

1. What is soil composed of?

_____

2. Why do the Minerals and Rocks circles intersect?

_____

3. Why don't the Humus and Rock circles overlap?

_____

_____

4. Explain what a grain is and give one reason why it is important.

_____

_____

_____

© NGSP & HB

Guided Inquiry

Investigate Soil and Water

 **Which kind of soil holds the most water?**

Make a Hypothesis

Which kind of soil will hold the most water? Write your hypothesis.

_____

_____

_____

Identify, Manipulate, and Control Variables

Which variable will you change?

_____

_____

Which variable will you observe or measure?

_____

_____

Which variables will you keep the same?

_____

_____

120

© NGSP & HB

Guided Inquiry   continued

Record

Write what you observe in the table below.

Soil and Water

	Kind of Soil _____	Kind of Soil _____
Observations		
Mass of dry soil and cup (g)		
Mass of wet soil and cup (g)		
Mass of water in soil (g)		

Guided Inquiry continued

Explain and Conclude

1. Do the results support your hypothesis? Explain.

_____

_____

_____

_____

_____

2. Compare your results with other groups. Which kind of soil holds the most water?

_____

_____

_____

_____

_____

© NGSP & HB

Guided Inquiry   continued

3. Infer why soils that hold a medium amount of water would be good for growing plants.

_____

_____

_____

_____

_____

Think of Another Question

What else would you like to find out about soil and water? How could you find an answer to this new question?

_____

_____

_____

_____

_____

© NGSP & HB

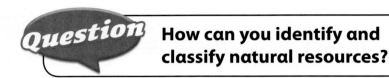

Investigate Natural Resources

How can you identify and classify natural resources?

Record

Write your observations and classifications in the table below.

Resource Uses and Classification

Resource	Uses	Renewable or Nonrenewable?
Rubber		

Directed Inquiry   continued

Resource Uses and Classification, continued

Resource	Uses	Renewable or Nonrenewable?

© NGSP & HB

Directed Inquiry continued

Use your data to make a graph that shows the number of renewable and nonrenewable resources you found.

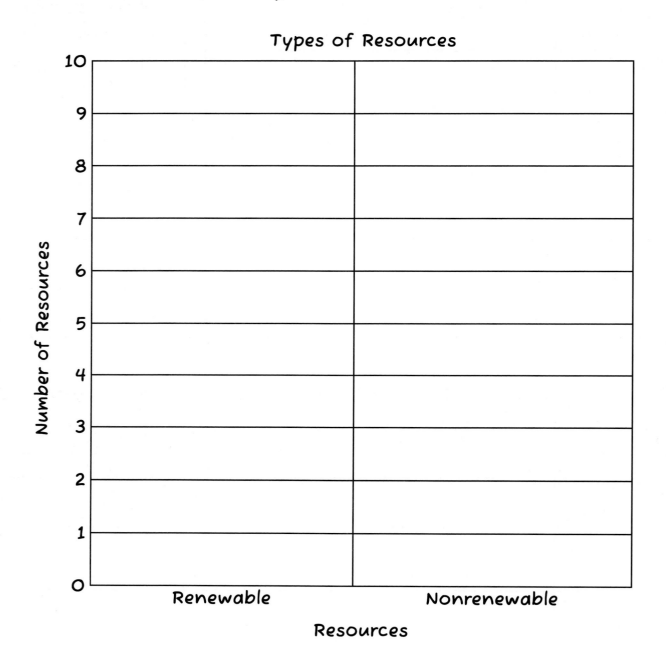

Directed Inquiry   continued

Explain and Conclude

1. Which resource has the most uses? Is this resource renewable or nonrenewable?

_____

_____

_____

_____

_____

2. Compare your data table with the class. Did you classify resources the same? What might you add to your table?

_____

_____

_____

_____

_____

Directed Inquiry continued

3. Look at the nonrenewable resources you found. How might you use fewer of these resources every day?

_____

_____

_____

_____

_____

Think of Another Question

What else would you like to find out about natural resources? How could you find an answer to this new question?

_____

_____

_____

_____

_____

Chapter 5 Science Vocabulary

Write one of the words or phrases from the box in each blank to complete the sentence.

fossil fuel	nonrenewable resources	natural resources
recycling	renewable resources	

1. Sunlight and air are _____.

2. _____ include metal and rocks.

3. Living and nonliving things found on Earth that people need are _____.

4. A nonrenewable resource that was formed from the remains of plants and animals is called _____.

5. Using an old object to make a new object is _____.

Write a caption describing the natural resources in this drawing. Use the terms *renewable resources* and *nonrenewable resources*.

_____

_____

_____

_____

_____

© NGSP & HB

Chapter 5 Share and Compare

1. Define *renewable resources* and *nonrenewable resources.*

2. List three renewable resources and three nonrenewable resources.

3. Choose one resource. Write a paragraph describing the resource, how we use it, and how we can care for it.

Earth's Natural Resources	
Renewable Resources	**Nonrenewable Resources**
1. Definition:	**1. Definition:**
2.	**2.**

3. Paragraph:

_____

_____

_____

_____

© NGSP & HB

Investigate Wind Energy

Question How can you use wind energy to move objects?

Record

Write your data in the table below.

Model Windmill

Number of Spoons	Number of Pennies Lifted

131

© NGSP & HB

Guided Inquiry continued

Explain and Conclude

1. Compare your data with your classmates. How did the number of spoons affect the test?

_____

_____

_____

_____

_____

2. Describe how the energy from your blowing lifted the objects in the cup.

_____

_____

_____

_____

_____

Guided Inquiry   continued

Think of Another Question

What else would you like to find out about wind energy? How could you find an answer to this new question?

_____

_____

_____

_____

_____

Name _____ Date _____

Investigate Features on a Map

**Question** **How can you use a map to identify land features?**

Record

Write your descriptions in the table below.

Land Features

Land Feature	Description
Mountain	
Valley	
Plain	
Canyon	

Directed Inquiry continued

Land Features, continued

Land Feature	Description
River	
Lake	

Explain and Conclude

1. How is the Land Features Map different from the Land Features Diagram?

_____

_____

_____

_____

_____

Directed Inquiry continued

2. Compare the different land features on the map. How does the map help you identify land features?

_____

_____

_____

_____

_____

3. Do you think the land features formed slowly or quickly? Explain.

_____

_____

_____

_____

_____

© NGSP & HB

my SCIENCE notebook

Directed Inquiry continued

Think of Another Question

What else would you like to find out about maps? How could you find an answer to this new question?

_____

_____

_____

_____

_____

_____

© NGSP & HB

Directed Inquiry continued

Land Features Diagram

Label these features on the diagram: Mountain, Canyon, Valley, Plain, River, and Lake.

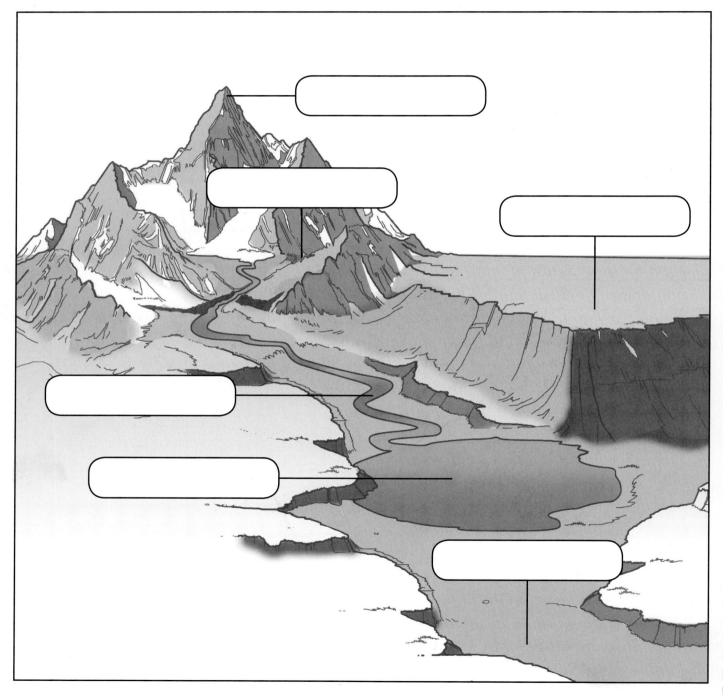

138

© NGSP & HB

Directed Inquiry continued

Land Features Map

Color the features on the map. Color the lakes blue and the rivers purple. Make the mountains brown and the plains yellow. Fill in the correct colors on the Map Key.

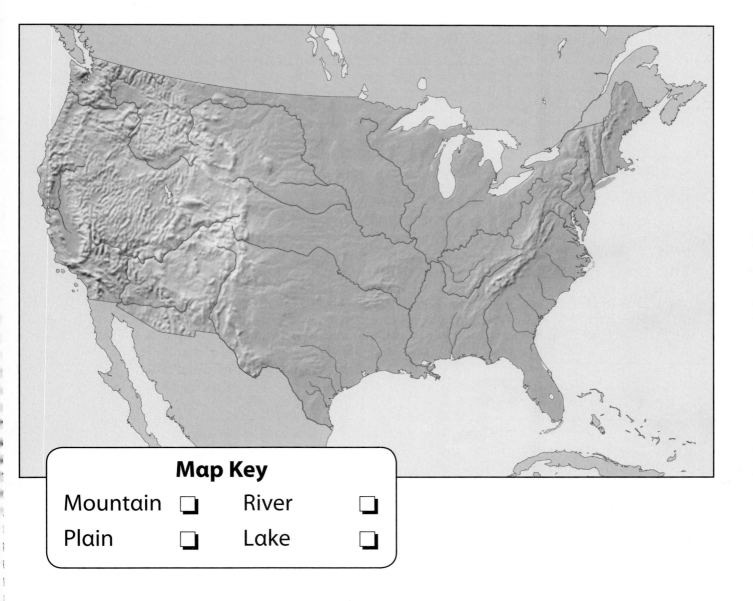

Map Key

Mountain ❑   River ❑

Plain ❑   Lake ❑

Chapter 6 Science Vocabulary

Write one of the words from the box in each blank to complete the sentence.

deposition	**erosion**	**glacier**	**landform**	**weathering**

1. A(n) _____ moves slowly, picking up soil and rock.

2. A plateau is a(n) _____ that has a flat top.

3. A beach may form by _____ of sand.

4. _____ breaks large rocks into small ones.

5. Rivers form valleys by _____ of rocks and soil.

6. The picture below shows large rocks. In the empty box next to the picture, draw what the rocks might look like after weathering happens for many years. Then on the lines below the boxes, write a sentence describing what happens to rocks as they weather.

_____

_____

© NGSP & HB

Chapter 6 Extend Learning

Investigate How Wind Changes Land

 **How did the wind change the land?**

In the boxes below, draw the sand dunes you observed in each pan.

Pan A

Pan B

1. How were the sand dunes in Pan A different from Pan B?

_____

2. Explain why the objects in Pan B made the sand dunes different.

_____

_____

3. How did changing the speed of the air make the sand dunes different?

_____

4. How did changing the direction of the air make the sand dunes different?

_____

© NGSP & HB

Chapter 6 Share and Compare

1. The landforms in the box below were caused mostly by erosion, weathering, or deposition. Fill in the web by writing each word in the correct circle. You may use the words more than once.

| valley | canyon | sand dune | Devil's Tower | beach |

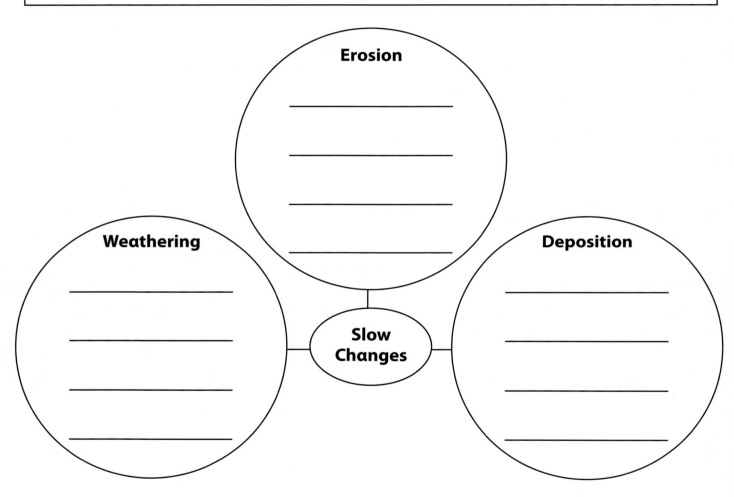

Erosion

_____

_____

_____

_____

Weathering

_____

_____

_____

_____

Deposition

_____

_____

_____

_____

Slow Changes

2. Choose a land feature that was caused by weathering. Explain how weathering caused this feature.

_____

_____

© NGSP & HB

Investigate Glaciers

Question How can you make a model to show what happens when glaciers move?

Predict

What will happen when the model glacier flows over soil, sand, and rocks? Write your prediction.

_____

_____

_____

_____

_____

_____

_____

143

© NGSP & HB

Record

Write and draw your observations in the table below.

Glacier Model Observations

What I Observed	What Happened
Model of Earth's features without glacier	
Model of Earth's features with glacier	

Guided Inquiry continued

Explain and Conclude

1. Did your results support your prediction? Explain.

_____

_____

_____

_____

_____

2. Compare your results with those of other groups. Did the glacier flow the same way in other models? What might cause differences?

_____

_____

_____

_____

_____

145

© NGSP & HB

Guided Inquiry continued

3. How is your model like a real glacier? How is it different?

_____

_____

_____

_____

_____

_____

Think of Another Question

What else would you like to find out about glaciers? How could you find an answer to this new question?

_____

_____

_____

_____

_____

_____

© NGSP & HB

Investigate Plate Movements

Question **What are ways Earth's plates can move?**

Record

Write and draw your observations in the table below.

Model Plate Movements

Movement	Observations

© NGSP & HB

Directed Inquiry   continued

Explain and Conclude

1. Describe three ways Earth's plates can move.

_____

_____

_____

_____

_____

2. The melted rock under Earth's surface is very hot. What do you think would happen to real melted rock below Earth's surface if the Earth's plates moved apart as the model plates did in step 3?

_____

_____

_____

_____

_____

148

© NGSP & HB

Directed Inquiry continued

3. What happened to the plates when you moved them together in step 4? How do you think Earth's surface changes when real plates move together?

_____

_____

_____

_____

Think of Another Question

What else would you like to find out about plate movements? How could you find an answer to this new question?

_____

_____

_____

_____

_____

149

© NGSP & HB

Chapter 7 Science Vocabulary

Circle the word that completes each sentence correctly. Then write the word on the line.

1. A(n) _____ is a piece of Earth's crust that slowly moves.

plate   magma

2. _____ is melted rock below Earth's surface.

Magma   Lava

3. _____ are a shaking of the ground.

Earthquakes   Volcanoes

4. Melted rock above Earth's surface is called _____.

lava   a plate

5. A(n) _____ is an opening in Earth's crust.

plate   volcano

Draw a volcano. Label the lava and magma.

[drawing box]

Write a sentence using *earthquake* and *plates*.

_____

© NGSP & HB

Chapter 7 Extend Learning

Model a Tornado

 **What is the shape of a tornado?**

Watch your teacher model this activity first. Then try the activity and answer the following questions.

1. What shape does the water form when you stir it?

_____

_____

2. What does this shape model?

_____

_____

3. What happens to the food coloring when you add it?

_____

_____

Chapter 7 Share and Compare

Use the words in the box to complete the cause-and-effect diagrams.

earthquakes   volcanoes   blizzards   thunderstorms   wildfires

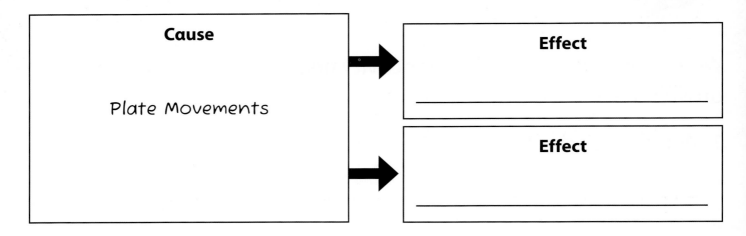

Cause

Plate Movements

→ **Effect**

_____

→ **Effect**

_____

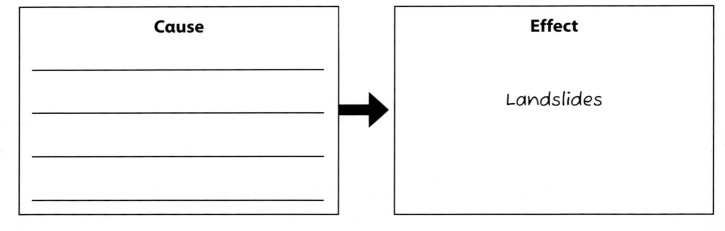

Cause

_____

_____

_____

→ **Effect**

Landslides

Cause

Lightning

→ **Effect**

_____

152

© NGSP & HB

Investigate Landslides

Question How can you model the way earthquakes and rainfall affect landslides?

Record

Write your choices and observations in the table below.

Landslides

	Earthquakes	Heavy Rain
Choice		
Observations		

 continued

Explain and Conclude

1. How did the force of the shaking and the speed of the pouring affect the landslides?

_____

_____

_____

_____

_____

2. Use the results of this investigation to infer what can cause real landslides to happen.

_____

_____

_____

_____

_____

_____

© NGSP & HB

Guided Inquiry   continued

Think of Another Question

What else would you like to find out about landslides? How could you find an answer to this new question?

_____

_____

_____

_____

_____

_____

Investigate Condensation

Question **How can you observe condensation and frost?**

Record

Write and draw your observations in the table below.

Metal Cans

Can	After 2 Minutes		After 3 More Minutes	
	Temperature (°C)	Observations	Temperature (°C)	Observations
Ice and salt				
Ice and water				

Directed Inquiry   continued

Explain and Conclude

1. Look for patterns in your data. What do you think caused the condensation on the cans?

_____

_____

_____

_____

2. Compare your observations of the 2 cans. Which can formed water on the outside faster? Which can formed frost? What do you think caused the differences?

_____

_____

_____

_____

_____

Directed Inquiry   continued

3. How does this investigation model what happens in the water cycle?

_____

_____

_____

_____

_____

Think of Another Question

What else would you like to find out about condensation? How could you find an answer to this new question?

_____

_____

_____

_____

© NGSP & HB

Chapter 8 Science Vocabulary

Complete the graphic organizer with the words from the box.

| condensation | evaporation | freezing |
| fresh water | salt water | |

Water can be either

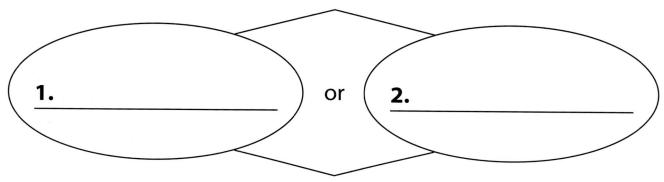

1. _____   or   2. _____

and can move and change by

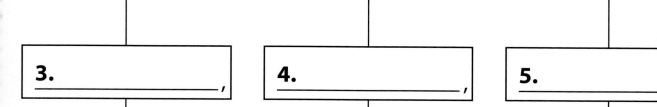

3. _____,

4. _____,

5. _____,

or change from a gas to a liquid.

or change from a liquid to a gas.

or change from a liquid to a solid.

© NGSP & HB

Chapter 8 Share and Compare

Complete the graphic organizer with the steps of the water cycle from the box below.

groundwater	**clouds**	**precipitation**
evaporate	**condenses**	

3. Tiny drops of water or crystals of ice form

_____.

4. Water or ice falls to Earth as

_____.

2. Water cools and

_____

as it rises higher into the air.

5. Water hits the ground and becomes runoff or

_____.

1. The sun's heat makes water on Earth's surface

_____.

Investigate Evaporation

Question How can you make water evaporate more quickly?

Record

Write your predictions and observations in the table below.

Water on Paper Squares

		Prediction	Time to Dry (s)
Trial 1	Square waved in air		
	Square on desk		
Trial 2	Crumpled square		
	Flat square		

Guided Inquiry continued

Water on Paper Squares, continued

		Prediction	Time to Dry (s)
Trial 3	Square in sunlight		
	Square in shade		
Trial 4	What is your plan?		

162

© NGSP & HB

Guided Inquiry   continued

Explain and Conclude

1. What can you conclude about what makes water evaporate more
quickly?

_____

_____

_____

_____

_____

2. Compare your data from step 6 with the data from other groups.
What did you do to your paper to make it dry more quickly?
What did the group with the fastest drying time do?

_____

_____

_____

_____

© NGSP & HB

Guided Inquiry continued

3. Use your observations to infer whether water from a lake would evaporate more quickly on a windy day or a calm day. Where would the water from the lake go?

_____

_____

_____

_____

_____

_____

Think of Another Question

What else would you like to find out about evaporation? How could you find an answer to this new question?

_____

_____

_____

_____

© NGSP & HB

Open Inquiry

Do Your Own Investigation

Open Inquiry Checklist

❏ Choose a question or make up one of your own.

_____

_____

❏ Gather the materials you will use.

_____

_____

_____

_____

❏ If needed, make a hypothesis or a prediction.

_____

_____

_____

_____

165

© NGSP & HB

Open Inquiry continued

❏ If needed, identify, manipulate, and control variables.

_____

_____

_____

_____

❏ Make a plan for your investigation.

_____

_____

_____

_____

_____

_____

_____

_____

© NGSP & HB

Open Inquiry continued

❏ Carry out your plan.

❏ Collect and record data. Analyze your data.

Open Inquiry   continued

❏ Explain and share your results.

_____

_____

_____

_____

_____

❏ Tell what you conclude.

_____

_____

_____

_____

❏ Think of another question.

_____

_____

_____

© NGSP & HB

Open Inquiry

SAMPLE QUESTION AND STEPS

Investigate Prisms

 **How do the colors in sunlight compare to the colors in light from a flashlight?**

Materials

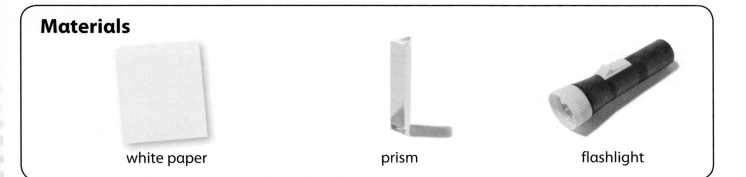

white paper   prism   flashlight

What to Do

1 Put the white paper in a very sunny place. Place the prism on the end of the paper closest to the sun. The prism should stand upright as shown in the picture.

What to Do, continued

2 Observe the light that shines through the prism. Slowly twist and turn the prism until you see a band of colored light. What colors do you see? Record your observations.

3 Move the white paper to a darkened area. Place the prism in the center of the paper.

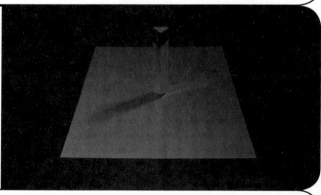

4 Shine the flashlight on the prism. Move the flashlight around the prism, and observe how the light changes as it passes through the prism. Keep moving the flashlight until you see a band of colors. What colors do you see? Record your observations.

© NGSP & HB

Science and Technology

Using Solar Energy

What Did You Find Out?

1. What is solar energy?

_____

_____

_____

2. Why is solar energy a good source of energy?

_____

_____

_____

3. How is solar energy used?

_____

_____

_____

 continued

Observe Solar Energy

Answer these questions about the rocks you placed in the sun for 30 minutes. Which rock feels the warmest?

_____

_____

_____

_____

Explain why you think this is so.

_____

_____

_____

_____

_____

_____

_____

© NGSP & HB

Science at Home

Dear Family,

In this *Physical Science* unit, your child is learning about matter, energy, forces, motion, and light. Please use this page to talk with your child about matter, the changes it goes through, and the different forces and forms of energy in your home.

Big Ideas

Your child is learning these important ideas:

- Matter is anything that has mass and takes up space. Properties of matter include size, color, shape, texture, and hardness. Mass is the amount of matter in an object. Volume is the amount of space that matter takes up.

- Solid, liquid, and gas are different states of matter. Matter changes state when its temperature changes. Freezing and condensation happen when water is cooled. Melting, boiling, and evaporation happen when water is heated.

- A force is a push or pull. Forces change the motion of objects. Friction is a force that works against the motion of objects that rub together. Earth's gravity is a force that pulls objects to the center of Earth.

- An object in a position where it may be pulled by gravity has stored energy. When the object begins moving it has energy of motion. The mechanical energy of the object is its stored energy plus its energy of motion. Sound is energy that travels in waves and can be heard. Electricity is energy that flows through wires and powers devices. Heat is the flow of energy from a warmer object to a cooler one.

- Light is energy we see. Light bouncing off an object is reflection. Light bending as it passes from one kind of matter to another is refraction. When we see an object, we see the color of light it is reflecting but not the colors of light it is absorbing. When an object blocks light's path, a shadow forms.

Share and Learn

With your child, list objects in your home and describe them in terms of size, color, shape, texture, and hardness. (You might make a guessing game of this.) List different states of water (water from the tap, ice in the freezer, water vapor from a humidifier, possibly frost on a windowpane). List the different forms of energy (light from a light bulb, sound from the TV, electrical wires).

家庭科学教育

亲爱的家长:

在*自然科学*这一单元中, 您的孩子将了解有关物质、能量、力、运动和光的知识。请按照本页所提供的方法, 与您的孩子讨论家中的物质、物质的变化、各种力和能量的不同形态。

概念

您的孩子将学到以下这些重要的概念:

- 物质是具有质量和体积的实物。物质的特性有大小、颜色、形状、结构和硬度。质量是物体中物质的量。体积是物质所占空间的大小。

- 固态、液态和气态是物质的不同形态。物质的形态随温度变化而变化。水冷却时会冻结并凝固。水加热时会融化、沸腾并蒸发。

- 力就是推力或拉力。力可以改变物体的运动。摩擦力是物体相对运动时产生的阻力。地球的重力是一种将物体拉向地心的力。

- 受到引力却保持静止的物体具有势能。物体开始移动便具有了动能。物体的机械能等于物体的势能加上动能。声音是通过波传递的一种能量, 我们可以听到声音。电能通过电线和供电设备流动。热是能量从温度较高物体到温度较低物体的转移。

- 光是我们可以看到的能量。光在物体上的散射叫做反射。光从一种物质进入到另一种物质时会变弯, 叫做折射。观察物体时, 我们看到的颜色是光反射的颜色, 而不是吸收了的颜色。物体挡住光的路径时, 就会出现影子。

分享和学习

和您的孩子一起, 列举家中的物体, 并按照大小、颜色、形状、结构和硬度进行描述。(可以就此做一个猜谜游戏。)列举水的不同形态 (水龙头中的水、冰库中的冰、增湿器中的水蒸汽, 或者玻璃窗上的白霜)。列举能量的不同形态 (灯泡发出的光、电视机中播放的声音、电线)。

Syans Lakay

Bonjou Fanmi,

Nan seksyon *Syans Fizik* sa a, pitit ou pral aprann enfòmasyon sou matyè, enèji, fòs, mouvman, ak limyè. Tanpri, itilize paj sa a pou pale avèk pitit ou sou matyè, sou chanjman li sibi, ak sou diferan fòs ak fòm enèji ki nan kay ou.

Enfòmasyon enpòtan

Men ki enfòmasyon enpòtan pitit ou ap aprann:

- Matyè se nenpòt bagay ki gen mas e ki pran espas. Pwopriyete matyè, ki enkli gwosè, koulè, fòm, teksti ak dite. Mas se kantite matyè ki genyen nan yon objè. Volim se kantite espas matyè pran.

- Solid, likid ak gaz se twa kondisyon fizik matyè ka genyen. Matyè chanje kondisyon fizik lè tanperati l chanje. Friz ak kondansasyon rive lè dlo rafrechi. Fonn, bouyi, epi evaporasyon rive lè dlo chofe.

- Yon fòs se yon pouse oubyen yon rale. Fòs chanje mouvman objè yo. Friksyon se yon fòs ki travay kont mouvman objè ki fwote youn ak lòt. Gravite ki gen sou Latè a se yon fòs ki rale tout bagay nan direksyon mitan Latè a.

- Yon objè ki nan yon pozisyon kote gravite ka rale l gen enèji ki konsève. Lè objè a kòmanse bouje li gen enèji sinetik. Enèji mekanik objè a se enèji anmagazinnen l lan plis enèji sinetik li a. Son se enèji ki vwayaje atravè onn e ke yo ka tande. Elektrisite se enèji ki sikile atravè fil e ki pèmèt aparèy fonksyone. Chalè se sikilasyon enèji de yon objè ki pi cho a yon objè ki pi fret.

- Limyè se enèji nou wè. Limyè ki rebondi sou yon objè se refleksyon. Limyè ki koube lè lap pase de yon kalite matyè a yon lòt se refraksyon. Lè nou wè yon objè, nou wè koulè limyè li reflete a men pa koulè limyè li absòbe a. Lè yon objè bloke trajè limyè, yon lonbraj fòme.

Pataje epi Aprann

Ansanm avèk pitit ou, liste objè ki nan kay ou epi dekri yo selon gwosè, koulè, fòm, teksti, ak dite yo. (Ou ka fè yon jwèt devinèt pou sa.) Liste diferan eta fizik dlo (dlo ki sot nan tiyo, glas ki nan frizè a, vapè dlo ki nan yon aparèy imidifikatè, glas ki ka sou yon vit). Liste diferan fòm enèji (limyè ki nan yon anpoul, son ki nan televizyon, fil elektrik).

175

© NGSP & HB

집에서 하는 과학 공부

부모님께,
이번 *자연 과학* 단원에서는 물질, 에너지, 힘, 운동 에너지 그리고 빛에 대해 배웁니다. 이 페이지를 통하여 물질과 물질이 겪는 변화, 그리고 집안에서 볼 수 있는 여러가지 힘 및 에너지 형태에 대해 자녀와 이야기를 나누어 보세요.

개념

자녀는 다음과 같은 중요 개념을 배웁니다.

- 물질은 질량이 있고 공간을 차지하는 것을 말합니다. 물질의 특성으로는 크기, 색깔, 모양, 질감, 굳기 등이 있습니다. 질량은 어떤 물체에 포함되어 있는 물질의 양입니다. 부피는 물질이 차지하는 공간의 크기입니다.

- 물질은 고체, 액체 및 기체의 세 가지 형태로 존재합니다. 온도가 변하면 물질의 상태도 변화합니다. 물의 온도가 내려가면 결빙 및 응결 현상이 발생합니다. 물에 열을 가하면 녹거나 끓거나 증발하는 현상이 일어납니다.

- 힘이란 밀기 또는 끌어 당기기를 뜻합니다. 힘은 물체의 운동 상태를 변화시킵니다. 마찰은 서로 맞닿아 있는 물체의 운동을 방해하는 힘입니다. 지구의 중력이란 물체를 지구의 중심으로 끌어 당기는 힘입니다.

- 중력에 의해 끌어당겨지는 위치에 있는 물체는 위치 에너지를 가지고 있습니다. 이 물체가 움직이기 시작하면 운동 에너지를 가지게 됩니다. 즉, 물체의 역학적 에너지는 위치 에너지와 운동 에너지를 더한 것입니다. 소리는 파동의 형태로 전달되는 에너지이며, 귀로 들을 수 있습니다. 전기는 전선을 타고 흐르는 에너지이며 기기를 작동하게 합니다. 열은 따뜻한 물체에서 차가운 물체로 이동하는 에너지의 흐름입니다.

- 빛은 우리가 눈으로 보는 에너지입니다. 물체에 부딪쳐서 빛이 튕겨 나가는 것을 반사라고 합니다. 빛이 한 종류의 물질에서 다른 종류의 물질로 지나면서 구부러지는 현상을 굴절이라고 합니다. 어떤 물체를 볼 때 우리는 물체가 흡수하는 빛의 색깔이 아닌 반사되는 빛의 색깔을 보는 것입니다. 어떤 물체가 빛이 지나는 방향을 막으면 그늘이 생깁니다.

함께하며 배워요

자녀와 함께 집안에 있는 물체의 목록을 만들고 크기, 색깔, 모양, 질감, 굳기로 그 물체를 설명해 보세요. (목록을 가지고 정답 알아맞히기 놀이를 하셔도 좋습니다.) 물의 여러가지 상태에 대해 목록(수돗물, 냉장고의 얼음, 가습기에서 나오는 수증기, 유리창에 낀 성에)을 만들어 보세요. 에너지의 여러가지 형태에 대해 목록(전구의 빛, 텔레비전에서 나오는 소리, 전선)을 만들어 보세요.

© NGSP & HB

Учимся дома

Уважаемые родители!
При изучении раздела *Физика* ребенок узнает о веществе, энергии, силах, движении и свете. Материал на этой странице поможет вам организовать с ребенком беседу о веществе, изменениях, которым оно подвергается, различных силах и видах энергии в вашем доме.

Это надо знать ···

Ребенок сможет понять и усвоить следующие тезисы:

- Вещество — это все, что имеет массу и занимает пространство. К свойствам вещества относятся размер, цвет, форма, фактура и твердость. Масса — это количество вещества в объекте. Объем — это количество пространства, которое занимает вещество.

- Вещество может находиться в твердом, жидком или газообразном состоянии. Состояние вещества меняется при изменении его температуры. При охлаждении вода замерзает и становится твердой. При нагревании вода тает, кипит и испаряется.

- Прикладывая силу, предметы можно отталкивать и притягивать. Силы изменяют движение объектов. Трение — это сила, которая противодействует движению объектов, трущихся друг о друга. Гравитация, или земное притяжение, — это сила, которая притягивает объекты к центру Земли.

- Объект, находящийся в таком положении, в котором его можно сдвинуть силой притяжения, обладает запасенной энергией. Когда объект начинает движение, он приобретает энергию движения. Механическая энергия объекта равна сумме его запасенной энергии и энергии движения. Звук — это энергия, которая распространяется в виде волн и которую можно услышать. Электричество — это энергия, которая течет по проводам и обеспечивает питание приборов. Тепло — это поток энергии от более теплого объекта к менее теплому.

- Свет — это энергия, которую мы видим. Свет, отражающийся от объекта, называется отражением. Изменение направления света на границе разных сред называется преломлением. Когда мы видим объект, мы видим цвет света, который отражается объектом, но не видим цветов, которые поглощаются им. Когда объект закрывает путь свету, появляется тень.

Учимся вместе ···

Вместе с ребенком перечислите объекты в вашем доме и опишите их с точки зрения размера, цвета, формы, фактуры и твердости. (Можете сделать из этого игру на угадывание.) Перечислите различные состояния воды (вода из крана, лед в морозильнике, водяной пар из увлажнителя, возможно, иней на окне). Перечислите различные формы энергии (свет от лампы, звук из телевизора, электрические провода).

Las ciencias en casa

Estimada Familia,

En este capítulo de *Física*, su hijo/a aprende sobre la materia, la energía, las fuerzas, el movimiento y la luz. Utilicen esta página para hablar con su hijo/a sobre la materia, los cambios que experimenta y las diferentes fuerzas y formas de energía en su casa.

Ideas principales

Su hijo/a está aprendiendo estas importantes ideas:

- Materia es cualquier cosa que tiene masa y que ocupa espacio. Sus propiedades incluyen tamaño, color, forma, textura y dureza. La masa es la cantidad de materia en un objeto. Volumen es la cantidad de espacio que ocupa esa materia.

- Sólido, líquido y gaseoso son diferentes estados de la materia. La materia cambia de estado cuando cambia su temperatura. El agua se congela y se condensa cuando se enfría. El agua se derrite, hierve y se evapora cuando se calienta.

- Una fuerza es un empuje o un jalón. Las fuerzas cambian el movimiento de los objetos. La fricción es una fuerza que reduce la capacidad de movimiento de los objetos que están en contacto. La gravedad de la Tierra es una fuerza que jala todo hacia el centro de la Tierra.

- Un objeto que esté en una posición en la que pueda ser jalado por la gravedad tiene energía almacenada. Cuando el objeto comienza a moverse, tiene energía de movimiento. La energía mecánica del objeto es su energía almacenada más su energía de movimiento. El sonido es energía que viaja en ondas y que se puede escuchar. La electricidad es energía que fluye a través de cables y que suministra energía a los aparatos. El calor es el flujo de energía de un objeto más caliente hacia uno más frío.

- La luz es energía que vemos. Se llama reflexión cuando la luz se refleja en un objeto. Se llama refracción cuando la luz se refracta al pasar desde un tipo de materia hacia otro. Cuando vemos un objeto, vemos el color de la luz que refleja, pero no los colores de la luz que absorbe. Cuando un objeto bloquea el paso de la luz, se forma una sombra.

Compartir y aprender

Junto con su hijo/a, hagan una lista de los objetos en su casa y descríbanlos en términos de tamaño, color, forma, textura y dureza. (Puede convertir esto en un juego de adivinanzas). Hagan una lista de estados diferentes del agua (agua del grifo, hielo en el congelador, vapor de agua de un humidificador, tal vez escarcha en una ventana). Hagan una lista de las diferentes formas de energía (luz de un foco, sonido de la TV, cables eléctricos).

© NGSP & HB

Khoa Học ở Nhà

Thân gửi Quý Phụ Huynh,
Trong bài này *Khoa Học Vật Lý,* con em quý vị học về vật chất, năng lượng, lực, chuyển động, và ánh sáng. Xin hãy sử dụng trang này để nói chuyện với con em quý vị về vật chất, sự biến đổi của nó, các lực và các dạng năng lượng khác nhau có trong nhà quý vị.

Các Khái Niệm Quan Trọng

Con em của quý vị được học các khái niệm quan trọng sau đây:

- Vật chất là bất cứ thứ gì có khối lượng và chiếm dụng không gian. Các đặc tính của vật chất bao gồm có kích thước, màu sắc, hình dạng, kết cấu, và độ cứng. Khối lượng là lượng vật chất có trong một vật thể. Thể tích là lượng không gian mà vật chất chiếm dụng.

- Rắn, lỏng, và khí là các trạng thái khác nhau của vật chất. Vật chất thay đổi trạng thái khi nhiệt độ của nó thay đổi. Hiện tượng đóng băng và ngưng tụ xảy ra khi nước được làm nguội. Tan chảy, sôi, và bay hơi xảy ra khi nước được đun nóng.

- Một lực là một sức đẩy hay sức kéo. Các lực làm thay đổi sự chuyển động của các vật thể. Ma sát là một lực cản trở sự chuyển động của các vật thể cọ xát với nhau. Trọng lực của Trái Đất là một lực kéo tất cả mọi thứ xuống, hướng về phía tâm của Trái Đất.

- Một vật thể tích trữ năng lượng khi nó ở một vị trí có thể bị hút bởi trọng lực. Một vật có động năng khi nó bắt đầu di chuyển. Cơ năng của một vật là năng lượng tích trữ cộng với động năng của nó. Âm thanh là năng lượng di chuyển ở dạng sóng và có thể được nghe thấy. Điện là năng lượng chạy qua các sợi dây và các thiết bị điện. Nhiệt là dòng năng lượng chạy từ một vật tới một vật khác nguội hơn nó.

- Ánh sáng là năng lượng ta nhìn thấy. Ánh sáng nảy lên khỏi một vật được gọi là sự phản xạ. Ánh sáng bị uốn cong khi truyền từ một loại vật chất này sang một loại vật chất khác gọi là sự khúc xạ. Khi nhìn một vật thể, ta thấy màu của ánh sáng mà nó phản xạ nhưng không thấy được màu ánh sáng mà nó hấp thu. Bóng được tạo ra khi một vật chặn ngang đường truyền của ánh sáng.

Chia Sẻ và Học Tập

Cùng với con em bạn hãy liệt kê các vật trong nhà và mô tả kích thước, màu sắc, hình dạng, kết cấu, và độ cứng của chúng. (Bạn có thể tạo ra một trò chơi đoán vui về những điều này) Hãy liệt kê các trạng thái khác nhau của nước (nước từ vòi nước, nước đá trong tủ lạnh, hơi nước từ một máy giữ độ ẩm, hay sương đọng trên ô kính cửa sổ). Hãy liệt kê các dạng năng lượng khác nhau (ánh sáng từ bóng đèn, âm thanh từ máy vô tuyến truyền hình, các dây điện).

Explore Activity

Investigate Physical Properties

Question How can you use tools to investigate physical properties?

Record

Write your predictions in the table below.

Predictions

Material	How will my observations change when I use the microscope?	How will the material's physical properties change when I cut it?
Burlap		
Wool		
Sandpaper		
Paper towel		
Silk		

Explore Activity continued

Write and draw what you observe in the table below.

Observations of Physical Properties

Material	Before Cutting			After Cutting		
	Just Eyes	Hand Lens	Microscope	Just Eyes	Hand Lens	Microscope
Burlap						
Wool						
Sandpaper						
Paper towel						
Silk						

Explore Activity continued

Explain and Conclude

1. Did your results support your predictions? Explain.

_____

_____

_____

_____

_____

2. How did tools help you to better observe the objects?

_____

_____

_____

_____

_____

© NGSP & HB

Explore Activity   continued

3. Compare the physical properties of the large pieces of the materials with the physical properties of the very small pieces.

_____

_____

_____

_____

_____

_____

Chapter 1 · Science Vocabulary

Fill in the squares for each vocabulary word.

Matter

Write the definition.	Draw an example.	Use in a sentence.

Mass

Write the definition.	Draw an example.	Use in a sentence.

Volume

Write the definition.	Draw an example.	Use in a sentence.

Texture

Write the definition.	Draw an example.	Use in a sentence.

© NGSP & HB

Chapter 1 Extend Learning

Investigate Volume

 **How much space inside the box will the books occupy?**

Object	Measurements (cm)	Volume (cm³)
Box		
Book		
Book		
Book		

1. Predict how many books will fit inside the box. Test your prediction and record your results.

_____

_____

2. Why did you measure the inside instead of the outside of the box?

_____

3. Now you need to add some odd-shaped objects to the box of books. How can you measure these solids?

_____

_____

_____

_____

© NGSP & HB

Chapter 1 Share and Compare

Fill in the property boxes with the correct words from the box below.

Size	Shape and Color

Texture	Hardness

big	green	bumpy	fuzzy	hard	rectangle	red	ridged
rough	scaly	slimy	small	smooth	soft	square	

Write a short paragraph about an object using words from the boxes.

_____

_____

_____

© NGSP & HB

Investigate Volume and Mass

 **How can you compare the volume and mass of solid and liquid objects?**

Record

Write your observations of volume in the table below.

Volume

Object	Volume of Water (mL)	Volume of Water and Object (mL)	Volume of Object (mL)
Marble	20		
Rock	20		

Predict

Which do you think has the most mass—the marble, the rock, or 20 mL of water?

_____

_____

Directed Inquiry   continued

Record

Write your observations of mass in the table below.

Mass

Object	Mass of Cup (g)	Mass of Cup and Object (g)	Mass of Object (g)
Marble			
Rock			
Water			

© NGSP & HB

Directed Inquiry continued

Explain and Conclude

1. Compare the volume of the water, marble, and rock. Which had the most volume?

_____

_____

_____

_____

2. Which object had the most mass? Is that what you predicted? Explain.

_____

_____

_____

_____

_____

Directed Inquiry   continued

3. Share your results with others. Explain any differences.

_____

_____

_____

_____

_____

Think of Another Question

What else would you like to find out about comparing the volume and mass of solids and liquids? How could you find an answer to this new question?

_____

_____

_____

_____

_____

© NGSP & HB

Directed Inquiry

Investigate Water and Temperature

 **What happens to water as the temperature changes?**

Predict

What will happen to the water in the bags when you put the bags in the freezer in step 2?

_____

_____

_____

_____

What will happen to the water in the bags when you put the bags in sunlight in step 5?

_____

_____

_____

_____

Directed Inquiry   continued

Record

Write or draw what you observe in the table below.

Observations of Bags with Water

	Bag 1	Bag 2
After 1 day in the freezer		
After 30 minutes on the desk		
After 1 day in sunlight		
After 2 days in sunlight		
After 3 days in sunlight		

© NGSP & HB

Directed Inquiry   continued

Explain and Conclude

1. Did your results support your predictions? Explain.

_____

_____

_____

_____

_____

2. Compare your results with the results of other groups. What patterns do you see?

_____

_____

_____

_____

_____

© NGSP & HB

Directed Inquiry   continued

3. Use your results from steps 2–6 to conclude what happens to water when the temperature goes down. What happens to frozen water when the temperature goes up?

_____

_____

_____

_____

_____

Think of Another Question

What else would you like to find out about what happens to water as the temperature changes? How could you find an answer to this new question?

_____

_____

_____

_____

© NGSP & HB

Chapter 2 Science Vocabulary

Write the word that fits each description. Use the words in the box.
You will use some words more than once.

states of matter solid liquid gas evaporation condensation

1. Always keeps its shape: _____

2. Gas changes to a liquid: _____

3. Solid, liquid, gas: _____

4. Takes the shape of its container: _____

5. Liquid changes to a gas: _____

6. Spreads out to fill a space: _____

7. Water vapor turns to drops of water: _____

8. Liquid water turns to water vapor: _____

Complete the chart with vocabulary words.

States of Matter	Ways the State of Matter Changes

Chapter 2 Share and Compare

Complete the chart with details from the box below.

Water

States	Properties	Changes to
		a liquid: _____
		a solid: _____ a gas: _____ or _____
		a liquid: _____

Details

boiling	gas	solid
condensation	keeps its shape	spreads to fill a space
evaporation	liquid	takes the shape of its container
freezing	melting	

 **Math in Science**

Measuring Temperature

What Did You Find Out?

1. What are two reasons why scientists use thermometers to measure temperature?

_____

_____

_____

_____

2. What two scales are used to measure temperature? Which do scientists usually use?

_____

_____

_____

_____

© NGSP & HB

 continued

Measure the Temperature of Water

What was the temperature of the water on both the Fahrenheit and Celsius scales?

Fahrenheit: _____

Celsius: _____

What was the temperature of the water in your partner's cup on both the Fahrenheit and Celsius scales?

Fahrenheit: _____

Celsius: _____

How did your temperature readings compare with your partner's readings? What might cause differences between the measurements?

_____

_____

_____

_____

_____

© NGSP & HB

Guided Inquiry

Investigate Melting

Question How does heating and cooling affect the properties of different materials?

Make a Hypothesis

What will happen to the temperature and properties of the frozen materials as they sit in sunlight? Write your hypothesis.

_____

_____

_____

Identify, Manipulate, and Control Variables

Which variable will you change?

_____

Which variable will you observe or measure?

_____

Which variables will you keep the same?

_____

_____

_____

Guided Inquiry continued

Record

Write what you observe in the table below.

Liquid in Cups

	Water		My Choice: _____	
	Temperature	Observations	Temperature	Observations
Before freezing				
After freezing				
After 10 min in sunlight				
After 20 min in sunlight				
After 30 min in sunlight				
After 40 min in sunlight				

© NGSP & HB

Guided Inquiry   continued

Explain and Conclude

1. What happened to the temperature of the liquids in the freezer?
   What happened to the temperature of the materials in sunlight?

   _____

   _____

   _____

   _____

2. How did the properties of the materials change as their
   temperatures changed? Do these results support your hypothesis?
   Explain.

   _____

   _____

   _____

   _____

   _____

Guided Inquiry continued

3. Compare the results of all groups. What patterns do you observe?

_____

_____

_____

_____

_____

_____

Think of Another Question

What else would you like to find out about changes in temperature and properties of materials? How could you find an answer to this new question?

_____

_____

_____

_____

_____

Name _____ Date _____

Directed Inquiry

Investigate Forces and Motion

Question How do forces affect motion?

Record

Write what you observe in the table below.

Motion of Ball

Trial	Prediction (cm)	How Far Ball Moves (cm)
Low ramp on floor		
High ramp on floor		
Low ramp on fabric		
High ramp on fabric		

203

© NGSP & HB

Directed Inquiry continued

Explain and Conclude

1. Did your results support your predictions? Explain.

_____

_____

_____

_____

_____

_____

2. Compare how the ball moved when you rolled it down the low and the high ramp. What do you think caused the difference?

_____

_____

_____

_____

_____

_____

© NGSP & HB

Directed Inquiry continued

3. Compare how the ball moved on the floor and on the fabric. What do you think caused the difference?

_____

_____

_____

_____

_____

Think of Another Question

What else would you like to find out about forces and motion? How could you find an answer to this new question?

_____

_____

_____

_____

Chapter 3 Science Vocabulary

Write the word that completes each sentence. Use the words in the box.

force	friction	gravity	magnetism	motion	speed

1. When an object is moving, it is in _____.

2. The distance an object moves in a period of time is the object's _____.

3. A push or a pull is a _____.

4. A force that acts when two surfaces rub together is _____.

5. A force that pulls an object to the center of Earth is _____.

6. A force between magnets and the objects magnets attract is _____.

7. How are gravity and magnetism alike?

_____

_____

_____

8. How are all forces alike?

_____

_____

© NGSP & HB

Investigate Changes in Motion

 **How can an object's motion change?**

Make a list of ways a moving object's motion can change.

_____

_____

_____

Record the changes in motion you observed in the table. Identify and describe each change.

Change Observed	Description
The ball changed direction.	The ball hit the wall. Then it moved in the opposite direction.

Share your observations with other groups. Then summarize the ways that an object's motion can change.

_____

_____

Chapter 3 Share and Compare

Classify each word in the box as a force or a change in motion. Then write each word in the table.

direction	friction	gravity	magnetism
position	pull	push	speed

Forces	Changes in Motion

Compare two forces. How are they alike?

_____

_____

Contrast two forces. How are they different?

_____

_____

_____

Choose an object that a force can move. Describe the object's position. Explain what force or forces can cause the object to move or to change its motion.

_____

_____

© NGSP & HB

Guided Inquiry

Investigate Motion and Position

Question How can you describe the motion of an object by observing its position?

Record

How will you move the ball from circle A to circle C? Write your plan. Be sure to list the materials you will use and the steps you will take to move the ball.

_____

_____

_____

_____

_____

_____

Guided Inquiry   continued

Write your data in the table below.

Path of Ball

Trial	Distance from Circle B (cm)
1	
2	
3	

Explain and Conclude

1. How did the ball's position change in relation to circle A? How did it change in relation to circle C?

_____

_____

_____

_____

© NGSP & HB

Guided Inquiry   continued

2. Compare your data. In which trial did the ball come closest to circle B? Describe the path of the ball in that trial. Describe the ball's position in relation to circle B.

_____

_____

_____

_____

_____

3. Conclude how you can use position to describe motion.

_____

_____

_____

_____

_____

Guided Inquiry continued

Think of Another Question

What else would you like to find out about motion and position? How could you find an answer to this new question?

_____

_____

_____

_____

_____

_____

Investigate Energy of Motion

Question How does adding more washers affect the motion of a pendulum?

Record

Write what you predict and observe in the table below.

Pendulum Swings

Number of Washers	Prediction	Number of Swings
1		
3		
5		

© NGSP & HB

Directed Inquiry continued

Use your data to make a bar graph below.

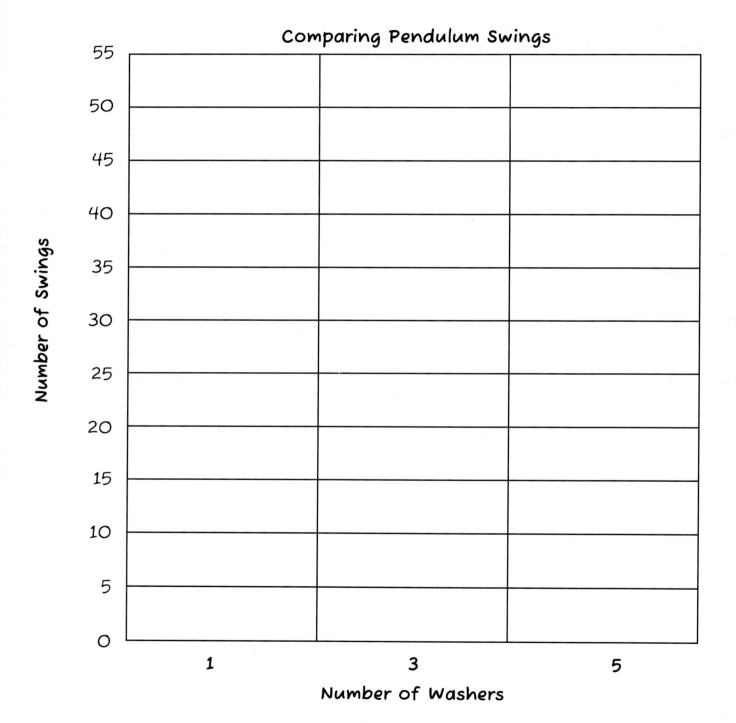

Comparing Pendulum Swings

Number of Swings

55
50
45
40
35
30
25
20
15
10
5
0

1   3   5

Number of Washers

Directed Inquiry   continued

Explain and Conclude

1. Did your results support your predictions? Explain.

_____

_____

_____

_____

_____

2. Compare the number of swings the pendulum made with 1, 3, and 5 washers. How did increasing the number of washers affect the motion of the pendulum?

_____

_____

_____

_____

_____

Directed Inquiry   continued

3. Describe the motion of the pendulum. Where in its swing does the pendulum move fastest? Where does it move slowest?

_____

_____

_____

_____

_____

_____

Think of Another Question

What else would you like to find out about how adding more washers can affect the swing of a pendulum? How could you find an answer to this new question?

_____

_____

_____

_____

216

© NGSP & HB

Chapter 4 Science Vocabulary

Write one of the words from the box in each blank to complete the sentence.

electricity	energy	mechanical energy	heat	sound

1. A car driving down a hill has _____.

2. An oven bakes food using _____ energy.

3. _____ is the ability to do work or cause a change.

4. DVD players need _____ to make them work.

5. When someone talks, we hear _____.

Write a caption for the drawing. Use the words *energy* and *heat*.

_____

_____

Chapter 4 Extend Learning

Investigate Mechanical Energy

 **How high will a ball bounce?**

Height (Stored Energy)	Prediction (Energy of Motion)	Observation (Energy of Motion)
0.5 m		
1 m		
1.5 m		

Analyze your data and record your conclusions below.

_____

_____

_____

_____

_____

© NGSP & HB

Chapter 4 Share and Compare

1. Write a definition for energy.

2. List the different types of energy in this chapter.

3. Write what you learned about each type of energy.

4. Write how people use each type of energy.

What Is Energy?		
_____		
Type of Energy	**Description**	**How People Use Energy**

Guided Inquiry

Investigate Vibrations and Sound

 **Question**   How does the length of a tuning fork affect the pitch of the sound it makes?

Record

Write what you observe in the table below.

Tuning Forks

Tuning Fork Length (cm)	What Happened to the Salt When You Touched the Tine to the Plastic Wrap?	Did It Make a Sound With a High or Low Pitch?

220

© NGSP & HB

Guided Inquiry   continued

Explain and Conclude

1. What happened to the salt when you touched the tuning forks to the plastic wrap? Explain why you think this happened.

_____

_____

_____

_____

_____

2. Compare the sounds made by the tuning forks. How did the length of the tuning fork affect the pitch of the sound it made?

_____

_____

_____

_____

_____

© NGSP & HB

Guided Inquiry continued

3. When an object vibrates faster, it makes a sound with a higher pitch than an object that is vibrating more slowly. Use your observations to infer which of your tuning forks vibrated faster.

_____

_____

_____

_____

_____

Think of Another Question

What else would you like to find out about vibrations and sound? How could you find an answer to this new question?

_____

_____

_____

_____

Directed Inquiry

Investigate Light and Heat

Question   **What happens to an object's temperature when light shines on it?**

Record

Write what you observe and predict in the table below.

Light and Temperature

	Temperature (°C)	Predictions
Start		What will happen to the temperature if you turn on the lamp?
Light on 5 minutes		What will happen to the temperature if you leave the lamp on for 5 more minutes?

Directed Inquiry   continued

Light and Temperature, continued

	Temperature (°C)	Predictions
Light on 10 minutes		What will happen to the temperature if you turn the lamp off?
Light off 5 minutes		What will happen to the temperature if you leave the lamp off for 5 more minutes?
Light off 10 minutes		

224

© NGSP & HB

Physical Science

Directed Inquiry   continued

Explain and Conclude

1. Did your observations support your predictions? Explain.

_____

_____

_____

_____

_____

2. What happened to the temperature as the lamp shined on the thermometer longer? What happened after you turned off the lamp?

_____

_____

_____

_____

© NGSP & HB

Directed Inquiry continued

3. What can you conclude about what can happen to the temperature of an object when light shines on it?

_____

_____

_____

_____

_____

Think of Another Question

What else would you like to find out about what happens to an object's temperature when light shines on it? How could you find an answer to this new question?

_____

_____

_____

_____

© NGSP & HB

Chapter 5 Science Vocabulary

Write two sentences about each of the words below. The first sentence should be the word's definition. The second sentence should give an example of the word. Share and discuss your sentences with your classmates.

1. light

_____

_____

2. reflection

_____

_____

3. refraction

_____

_____

4. absorption

_____

_____

© NGSP & HB

Chapter 5 Extend Learning

Shadows Where?

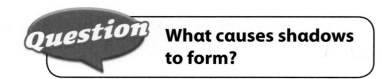

Question   **What causes shadows to form?**

1. Put the toy figures on the desk. Put the flashlight in the middle of the figures. Turn the flashlight on. In the box below, draw what you see.

[ ]

2. Move the flashlight to a new position. In the box below, draw what you see.

[ ]

How did the shadows change? Why did the shadows change?

_____

_____

_____

Chapter 5 Share and Compare

Use the words in the box to fill in the table. Each word can be used more than once.

reflection	refraction	absorption

Example	Property of Light
a rainbow in the sky	
a mirror that shows your image	
a black jacket that feels warmer after you stand in sunlight	
an office window that shows an image of the blue sky and white clouds	
a black asphalt driveway that feels hot to your bare feet	
rocks at the bottom of a clear pond with "bent" or "wavy" looking edges	

229

© NGSP & HB

Investigate Light and Objects

Question What happens to light when it shines on different objects?

Record

Write what you observe in the table below.

Light on Paper

Material Between Flashlight and Paper	Predictions	Observations	
	On the white paper	On the white paper	On the object
None			

Guided Inquiry continued

Light on Paper, continued

Material Between Flashlight and Paper	Predictions	Observations	
	On the white paper	On the white paper	On the object

Explain and Conclude

1. Compare how bright the light on the white paper was when you shined the flashlight at the 3 different objects.

_____

_____

_____

_____

_____

231

© NGSP & HB

Guided Inquiry   continued

2. Were you able to see the same amount of light on all 3 objects in step 5? Why do you think that is so?

_____

_____

_____

_____

_____

3. Based on the results of your investigation, what can you infer about what happens to light when it shines on different objects?

_____

_____

_____

_____

_____

_____

© NGSP & HB

Guided Inquiry continued

Think of Another Question

What else would you like to find out about what happens to light when it shines on different objects? How could you find an answer to this new question?

_____

_____

_____

_____

Open Inquiry

Do Your Own Investigation

Open Inquiry Checklist

❏ Choose a question or make up one of your own.

_____

_____

❏ Gather the materials you will use.

_____

_____

_____

_____

_____

❏ If needed, make a hypothesis or a prediction.

_____

_____

_____

Open Inquiry   continued

❑ If needed, identify, manipulate, and control variables.

_____

_____

_____

_____

❑ Make a plan for your investigation.

_____

_____

_____

_____

_____

_____

_____

Open Inquiry continued

❏ Carry out your plan.

❏ Collect and record data. Analyze your data.

Open Inquiry   continued

❏ Explain and share your results.

_____

_____

_____

_____

❏ Tell what you conclude.

_____

_____

_____

_____

❏ Think of another question.

_____

_____

_____

_____

_____

Open Inquiry

SAMPLE QUESTION AND STEPS

Investigate Evaporation

Question How can you make water evaporate more quickly?

Materials

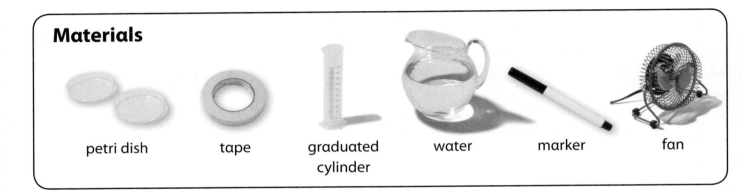

| petri dish | tape | graduated cylinder | water | marker | fan |

What to Do

1 Label half of the petri dish **Fan.** Label the other half **No Fan.**

What to Do, continued

2 Use the graduated cylinder to measure and pour 30 mL of water in each dish.

Fan

3 Observe the level of the water. Using tape and the marker, mark the water level in each dish.

Fan

4 Place both dishes in a sunny place. Place the fan so that it blows onto the water in the **Fan** dish. Make sure the fan does not blow on the **No Fan** dish.

5 Leave the fan on for one day. Then observe and compare the level of water in each dish. Which dish had more water evaporate?

How Scientists Work

Using Observations to Evaluate Explanations

What Did You Find Out?

1. What are three ways that scientists might organize their data?

_____

_____

_____

_____

_____

2. Why do scientists analyze their data?

_____

_____

_____

_____

© NGSP & HB

 continued

Evaluate Explanations

Rico's data are shown in the table below. Analyze the data, and then answer the question.

Mass of Water Balloons

Trial	Mass of Large Balloon	Mass of Small Balloon
1	615 g	246 g
2	615 g	246 g
3	615 g	246 g

Do you agree with Rico's idea that the bigger water balloon has more mass? Write a paragraph explaining your answer. Be sure to use Rico's data to support your argument.

_____

_____

_____

_____

_____

© NGSP & HB

Panel 1 (page 8)

Name _____ Date _____

Explore Activity

Investigate Plants and Gravity

Question How does gravity affect the growth of plant roots?

Predict

Lay cup A on its side. Do not change the position of cup B. In which direction will the roots of each plant grow? Write your prediction.

Possible answer: If I turn cup A sideways, then the roots will grow toward the side that is near the ground. If I do not move cup B, the roots will grow toward the bottom of the cup.

Turn cup A upright. Do not change the position of cup B. In which direction will the roots of each plant grow? Write your prediction.

Possible answer: If I turn cup A upright, then the roots will change direction and grow toward the bottom of the cup. If I do not move cup B, the roots will continue to grow toward the bottom of the cup.

Learning Master **8** Life Science
© NGSP & HB

Panel 2 (page 9)

Name _____ Date _____

Explore Activity continued

Record

Write and draw what you observe in the table below.

How Plant Roots Grow

Day	Cup A Observations	Cup B Observations
	Answers may vary. Students should observe that the roots in cup A changed direction when the cup was turned on its side. The number of days students observe the cups will depend on how quickly the plants sprout and grow. Students may continue their tables on separate sheets of paper as necessary.	

Learning Master **9** Life Science
© NGSP & HB

Panel 3 (page 10)

Name _____ Date _____

Explore Activity continued

Explain and Conclude

1. Do the results support your predictions? Use your observations to explain.

   Students' predictions will vary, but they may have predicted that cup A's roots would change direction when turned on its side.

2. Infer the way gravity affects the growth of plant roots. Tell what evidence from this activity you observed to make your inference.

   Possible answer: Gravity causes the roots of a plant to grow downward. No matter which way I turned the cup, the roots grew downward.

Learning Master **10** Life Science
© NGSP & HB

Panel 4 (page 11)

Name _____ Date _____

Chapter 1 Science Vocabulary

Write one of the vocabulary words in each blank to complete the sentence.

> environment
> germinate
> organism
> pollen
> reproduce
> spore

1. A plant, animal, or other living thing is called a(n) ___organism___ .

2. The male parts of a flower make ___pollen___ .

3. Seeds begin to grow when they ___germinate___ .

4. All of the living and nonliving things around an organism are its ___environment___ .

5. A tiny part of a moss or fern that can grow into a new plant is a(n) ___spore___ .

6. Most plants ___reproduce___ by making flowers, seeds, and fruits.

Write a sentence about this drawing. Use a vocabulary word.

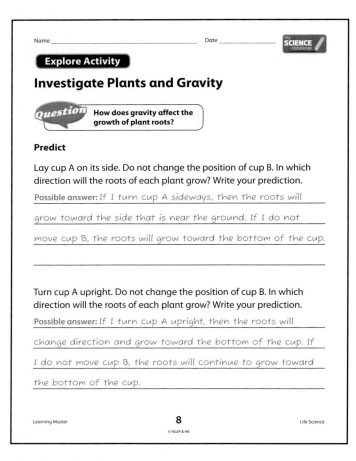

Possible answer: A seed is germinating.

Learning Master **11** Life Science
© NGSP & HB

Panel 1 (top left)

Chapter 1 Share and Compare

Draw pictures in each box to show the life cycle of an apple tree.

Life Cycle of an Apple Tree

Students' drawings should show the four stages in the life cycle of an apple tree. Students can label their drawings.

1. Germinating Seed

2. Seedling

4. Fruit

3. Flowering Tree

Panel 2 (top right)

Directed Inquiry

Investigate Plant Parts

Question How can you classify plants by their parts?

Record

Write and draw what you observe in the table below.

Observations of Plant Picture Cards

Sunflower	
Rye grass	
Corn	
Boston fern	Observations may vary. Students should observe the characteristics of the different types of plants.
Moss	
Bracken fern	

Panel 3 (bottom left)

Directed Inquiry continued

Write and draw what you observe in the table below.

Observations of Seeds and Spores

Sunflower seed	
Rye grass seed	Observations may vary. Students should observe the characteristics of the different types of seeds and spores.
Corn seed	
Spore slide	

Classify the plants on Picture Cards 7–9.

Classification of Plants

Plant	Seed-Producer or Spore-Producer?
Echinacea	seed-producer
Sword fern	spore-producer
Plumeria	seed-producer

Panel 4 (bottom right)

Directed Inquiry continued

Explain and Conclude

1. How are the plants on all the Picture Cards similar and different?

   Possible answer: All of the plants have roots, stems, and leaves. The shapes of the leaves are different. Some plants have flowers that produce seeds. Some plants do not have flowers, and they produce spores.

2. How did your observations of seeds and spores help you to classify the plants on Picture Cards 7–9?

   Answers will vary, but students may note that observing the seeds and spores on the slide helped them to identify which plants have the structures to produce seeds or spores.

Directed Inquiry continued

3. Share your classification with other groups. Talk about other ways that you could classify the plants on the Picture Cards.

Possible answer: I could classify the plants by the shape of

their leaves.

_____

_____

_____

_____

Think of Another Question

What else would you like to find out about the parts of plants? How could you find an answer to this new question?

Answers may vary. Record students' questions for possible future

investigations.

_____

_____

_____

Directed Inquiry

Investigate Animal Classification

Question How can you identify animals with backbones and model how a backbone works?

Record

Write and draw what you observe in the table below.

Animal Classification

Animal	Observations	Backbone or No Backbone?
Chimpanzee		backbone
Clownfish	Observations will vary, but students should describe each animal's body parts, body coverings, and other physical features.	backbone
Earthworm		no backbone
Horse		backbone
Snake		backbone

Directed Inquiry continued

Animal Classification continued

Animal	Observations	Backbone or No Backbone?
Squid		no backbone
Sea sponge	Observations will vary, but students should describe each animal's body parts, body coverings, and other physical features.	no backbone
Robin		backbone
Lobster		no backbone
Snail		no backbone

Observe

What did you observe as you bent and twisted your model backbone? Write your observations below.

Answers will vary. Students may have correctly observed that the parts of a

backbone move together when the backbone bends and twists.

_____

Directed Inquiry continued

Explain and Conclude

1. How did you use your observations to classify the animals as animals with backbones and animals without backbones?

Possible answer: I observed the animals' body parts and looked

to see which ones had sturdy but moveable bodies.

_____

_____

_____

2. Infer how the structure of the backbone helps an animal move different ways. Use your observations of the model backbone to explain your answer.

Possible answer: The parts of the backbone work together to

support the animal. The backbone can also bend and twist.

_____

_____

_____

Directed Inquiry continued

Think of Another Question

What else would you like to find out about animals with backbones and how their backbones work? How could you find an answer to this new question?

Answers may vary. Record students' questions for possible future

investigations.

Learning Master   **20**   Life Science
© NGSP & HB

Chapter 2 Science Vocabulary

Write one of the vocabulary words in each blank to complete the sentence.

backbone
classify
invertebrate
vertebrate

1. The ___backbone___ protects the main nerve cord in some animals.
2. Characteristics are used to ___classify___ organisms, or place them in groups.
3. A cheetah is a(n) ___vertebrate___ because it has a backbone.
4. A grasshopper is a(n) ___invertebrate___ because it does not have a backbone.

Classify each of these organisms as a vertebrate or invertebrate.

5. ___vertebrate___

6. ___invertebrate___

7. ___invertebrate___

8. ___vertebrate___

Learning Master   **21**   Life Science
© NGSP & HB

Chapter 2 Extend Learning

Classify Animals by Group

Choose an animal pictured in the Big Ideas Book. Write its name and draw it. Then answer the questions in the table. Your animal is classified in the group that has the most *yes* answers.

Animal: _____

Animals will vary depending on student choices.

Fish	Bird
Does it have a backbone? _____	Does it have a backbone? _____
Does it live in water? _____	Does it have feathers and two legs covered with scales? _____
Does it have fins, scales, and gills? _____	Does it have two wings? _____
Do the young hatch from eggs? _____	Do the young hatch from eggs? _____
Amphibian	**Mammal**
Does it have a backbone? _____	Does it have a backbone? _____
Does it live part of its life in water and part of its life on land? _____	Does it have hair or fur? _____
Does it have four legs and thin, damp skin? _____	Are the young born live? _____
Do the young hatch from eggs? _____	Does it make milk to feed its young? _____
Reptile	**Arthropod**
Does it have a backbone? _____	Does it have a hard outside skeleton instead of a backbone? _____
Is it covered in hard scales that are not shiny? _____	Does it have jointed legs? _____
Does it have lungs and breathe air? _____	Is its body divided into sections? _____
Do the young hatch from eggs? _____	Do the young hatch from eggs? _____

Learning Master   **22**   Life Science
© NGSP & HB

Chapter 2 Extend Learning continued

Draw an example of a vertebrate and an invertebrate. Then write one or two sentences that explain how they are different.

Vertebrate	Invertebrate

The vertebrate has a backbone, and the invertebrate does not.

Learning Master   **23**   Life Science
© NGSP & HB

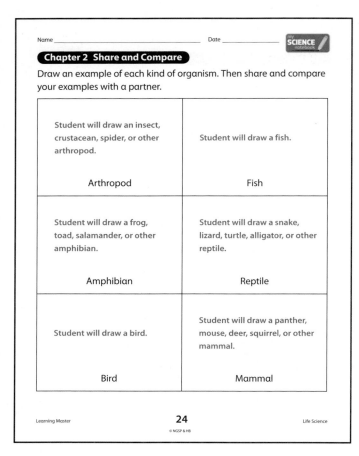

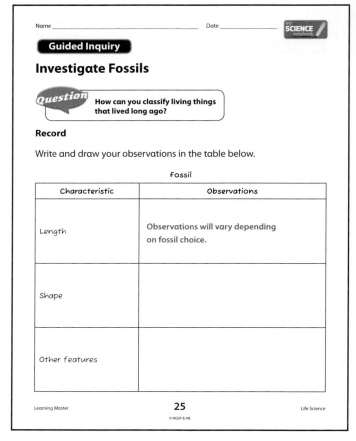

Chapter 2 Share and Compare

Draw an example of each kind of organism. Then share and compare your examples with a partner.

Student will draw an insect, crustacean, spider, or other arthropod. Arthropod	Student will draw a fish. Fish
Student will draw a frog, toad, salamander, or other amphibian. Amphibian	Student will draw a snake, lizard, turtle, alligator, or other reptile. Reptile
Student will draw a bird. Bird	Student will draw a panther, mouse, deer, squirrel, or other mammal. Mammal

Guided Inquiry

Investigate Fossils

Question How can you classify living things that lived long ago?

Record

Write and draw your observations in the table below.

Fossil

Characteristic	Observations
Length	Observations will vary depending on fossil choice.
Shape	
Other features	

Guided Inquiry continued

Explain and Conclude

1. Was your fossil animal an invertebrate or a vertebrate? What was its environment like? How do you know?

   Possible answer: The fossilized animal was an invertebrate that lived in water. It was like today's snails, which do not have backbones.

2. How else could you classify the fossils?

   Possible answer: I classified the fossils as animals that had shells and animals that did not have shells.

Guided Inquiry continued

Think of Another Question

What else would you like to find out about classifying living things that lived long ago? How could you find an answer to this new question?

Answers will vary. Record students' questions for possible future investigations.

Guided Inquiry continued

Investigate Fossils

Fossil Information

Fossil	What It Looks Like	What Scientists Know	Vertebrate or Invertebrate?
ammonite		• Shells were usually the only part that became fossils because the soft body was rarely preserved. • Their spiral-shaped shell was hard like today's snail shell. • They probably lived in open ocean water rather than at the bottom. • They ate other animals such as reptiles, softer shelled animals, and other small animals. They grabbed prey with tentacles.	invertebrate
shark tooth		• Teeth were usually the only part that became fossils because their skeletons were made of cartilage—the same kind of material that makes up your ears and the tip of your nose. • They lived in seas that covered what is now land. • They ate other animals that lived in the water.	vertebrate
trilobite		• They lived in oceans where they moved over the ocean floor looking for food. They ate other very small animals or living things that had died. • They belonged to the same group of animals as insects and lobsters. • Their outer covering was similar to that of a crab or lobster today. • They had a toothless mouth, but could suck water and prey into their mouths.	invertebrate

---

Guided Inquiry continued

Investigate Fossils

Fossil Information

Fossil	What It Looks Like	What Scientists Know	Vertebrate or Invertebrate?
fish		• Fish fossils are common in many parts of the world. There were many different kinds of fish that left behind fossils. • Many fossil fish resembled fish that live today.	vertebrate
gastropod		• They belonged to the same group of animals as snails and slugs. • Most fossils are of shells because they had very soft bodies. • The first gastropods lived in oceans. • They ate both plants and tiny animals that floated in water. • Inside the mouth was a feeding structure that was made up of thousands of tiny teeth-like structures that helped shred food.	invertebrate
crinoid stem		• Made of three sections, a tough stem filled with muscles, the major organs, and the arms. Usually only the stem formed fossils. • They filtered small particles of food from seawater with their feather-like arms. • They looked like plants, but were animals.	invertebrate

---

Directed Inquiry

Investigate Interactions in a Model Pond

Question How do living things in a model pond ecosystem interact?

Record

Write and draw what you observe in the table below.

Model Ecosystem

Model Pond Part	Observations	Living or Nonliving?	What I Infer About Its Needs	Producer or Consumer?
Sand	Observations will vary.	nonliving		
Elodea plant		living	Answers will vary.	producer
Rocks		nonliving		
Water		nonliving		
Snails		living	Answers will vary.	consumer

Directed Inquiry continued

Draw your model pond ecosystem. Circle the living things. Draw arrows to show how energy moves from the sun to the producers and consumers in the pond ecosystem.

My Model Pond Ecosystem

Drawings will vary, but should include the sun and all elements of the model pond. Students should circle the *Elodea* and snails. Students should draw arrows from the sun to the *Elodea* to the snails.

Explain and Conclude

1. How did your observations help you classify producers and consumers in your ecosystem?

   Possible answer: I observed the snail eating the *Elodea* plant, so I know the snail is a consumer. The *Elodea* plant needs sunlight to make its own food, so it is a producer.

Name _____ Date _____

Directed Inquiry continued

2. How did this model help you understand how living things in a real pond ecosystem interact?

Possible answer: I can observe the model pond to understand how living things in a real pond get energy.

Think of Another Question

What else would you like to find out about how living things interact in a pond ecosystem? How could you find an answer to this new question?

Answers may vary. Record students' questions for possible future investigations.

Name _____ Date _____

Chapter 3 Science Vocabulary

Write one of the vocabulary words in each blank to complete the sentence.

> community
> consumer
> decomposer
> food chain
> population
> producer

1. All the bison in one area make up a __population__.

2. All the living things in the same area form a __community__.

3. A grass plant is classified as a __producer__ because it makes its own food.

4. A wolf is classified as a __consumer__ because it eats other living things for food.

5. An earthworm is a __decomposer__ because it breaks down living things that have died.

6. An oak tree, caterpillar, robin, and bobcat form a __food chain__ in which energy passes from one organism to the next.

Label each organism in the diagram as a producer or consumer. Then write a caption to describe the diagram.

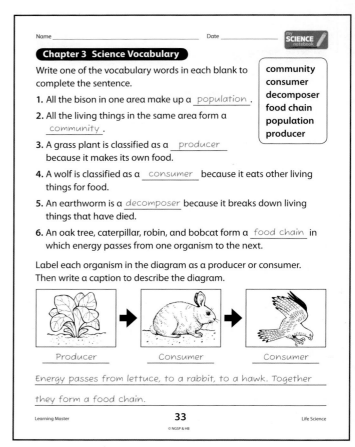

| Producer | Consumer | Consumer |

Energy passes from lettuce, to a rabbit, to a hawk. Together they form a food chain.

Name _____ Date _____

Chapter 3 Extend Learning continued

Herbivores	Carnivores	Omnivores
Rabbit, Zebra, Gypsy moth caterpillar	Coyote, Lion	Opossum, Robin

Predators	Prey
Coyote, Lion, Robin, Opossum	Rabbit, Zebra, Gypsy moth caterpillar

Write sentences to answer these questions.

1. How are herbivores and carnivores alike? How are they different?

   Both herbivores and carnivores are animals that must eat to gain energy. Herbivores eat plants only; carnivores eat meat only.

2. How are all the predators alike? How are they different?

   All the predators hunt and eat animals. Some are fierce and eat large animals; others eat small animals only.

3. How could an animal be both predator and prey?

   A robin could be the predator of a caterpillar, and it could be the prey for an opossum.

Name _____ Date _____

Chapter 3 Share and Compare

In the box, draw the three living things. Connect them with arrows to show a food chain. Label each living thing as a producer or consumer.

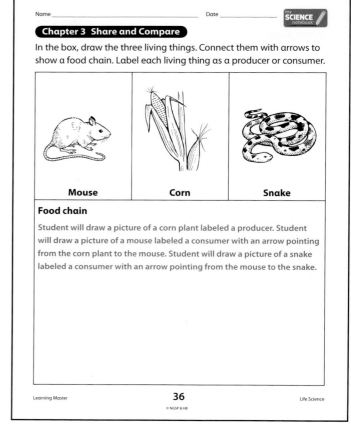

| **Mouse** | **Corn** | **Snake** |

Food chain

Student will draw a picture of a corn plant labeled a producer. Student will draw a picture of a mouse labeled a consumer with an arrow pointing from the corn plant to the mouse. Student will draw a picture of a snake labeled a consumer with an arrow pointing from the mouse to the snake.

Name _____ Date _____

Guided Inquiry

Investigate Brine Shrimp

Question How do different amounts of salt in the water affect hatching of brine shrimp eggs?

Make a Hypothesis

How will the amount of salt affect the number of brine shrimp eggs that hatch?

Possible answer: If I add more salt to the water, then fewer brine shrimp eggs will hatch.

Identify and Control Variables

Which variable will you change?

I will add different amounts of salt to each cup.

Which variable will you observe or measure?

I will observe how many brine shrimp eggs hatch in each cup.

Which variables will you keep the same?

Each cup will have the same amount of water. I will put the same amount of brine shrimp eggs in each cup. I will cover each cup with plastic wrap.

Name _____ Date _____

Guided Inquiry continued

Observe

What are your observations of the brine shrimp eggs in step 1?

Possible answer: They are small and brown.

_____

Record

Write what you observe in the table below.

Estimated Number of Brine Shrimp

	Cup 1: Control (1 ½ Spoonfuls of Salt)	Cup 2: ____ Spoonfuls of Salt	Cup 3: ____ Spoonfuls of Salt
Day 1			
Day 2		Answers will vary, but students should see the maximum number of shrimp hatched in the Control cup.	
Day 3			
Day 4			

Name _____ Date _____

Guided Inquiry continued

Explain and Conclude

1. Compare the number of brine shrimp that hatched in each cup.

   Results will vary, but students may observe that the most shrimp hatched in the Control cup. Students could also see hatching in the 1 and 2 spoonful cups. Minimal hatching should occur in the ½, 2 ½, and 3 spoonful cups.

2. What can you conclude about how different amounts of salt affect the hatching of brine shrimp eggs?

   Possible answer: I conclude that brine shrimp need salt to live. Brine shrimp do not hatch in water that has too much or too little salt.

Name _____ Date _____

Guided Inquiry continued

Think of Another Question

What else would you like to find out about how different amounts of salt affect brine shrimp? How could you find an answer to this new question?

Answers will vary. Record students' questions for possible future investigations.

Name _____ Date _____

Directed Inquiry

Investigate Plant Adaptations

Question **How does a leaf's covering affect how quickly it wilts?**

Record

Write and draw what you observe in the table below.

Comparing Leaves

Day and Time	Observations of Leaf With Waxy Coating	Observations of Leaf Without Waxy Coating
Start		
	Observations will vary, but students should describe each leaf's size, shape, color, surface, and other properties. Students should note any changes they observe over 2 days.	

Name _____ Date _____

Directed Inquiry continued

Predict

Which leaf will wilt more quickly in sunlight? Write your prediction.

Predictions will vary, but students may say that the leaf without the waxy coating will wilt more quickly than the leaf with the waxy coating.

Explain and Conclude

1. Do the results support your prediction? Explain.

   Possible answer: The results support my prediction that the leaf without the waxy coating would wilt more quickly than the leaf with the waxy coating.

Name _____ Date _____

Directed Inquiry continued

2. Share your results with others. Did they get the same results? Explain any differences.

   Answers will vary. Differences in students' results may have been caused by individual variation in leaves and location of leaves.

3. Infer which kind of leaf covering is more likely to be found on plants that live in a dry place.

   Possible answer: I infer that a leaf with a waxy coating would more likely be found in a dry place than a leaf without a waxy coating. A waxy coating keeps leaves from wilting as fast.

Name _____ Date _____

Directed Inquiry continued

Think of Another Question

What else would you like to find out how a plant's covering affects wilting? How could you find an answer to this new question?

Answers will vary. Record students' questions for possible future investigations.

Chapter 4 Science Vocabulary

adaptation	camouflage	instinct	mimicry

Write one of the vocabulary words in each blank to complete the sentence.

1. A mother fox has a(n) _instinct_ to find a den and protect her young.

2. The tail end of a caterpillar looks like a snake. This shows _mimicry_ .

3. The sharp claws and teeth of a grizzly bear are each a(n) _adaptation_ for getting food.

4. A chameleon has _camouflage_ because it blends in with its background.

Define the word **adaptation**. Use the cactus as an example.

An adaptation is a feature that
helps a living thing survive in
its environment. A cactus lives
in dry deserts. One of its
adaptations is a thick stem for
storing water.

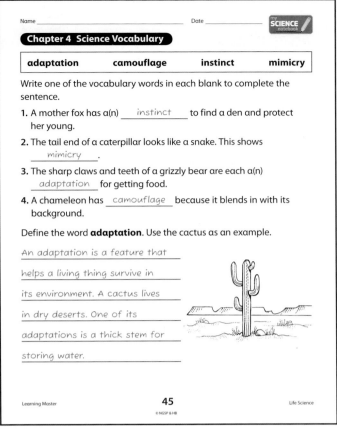

Chapter 4 Share and Compare

Complete each sentence to show how plants and animals adapt to survive. Use the words and phrases in the box.

channels
broad leaves
tongues
food
pollinators
stems
blubber
thorns

Plants	Animals
Rain forest plants have _broad leaves_ to take in sunlight.	Grizzly bears have sharp claws to grasp _food_ .
Cacti have thick _stems_ for storing water.	Chameleons use long, sticky _tongues_ to catch insects.
Blackberry bushes have _thorns_ for protection.	Seals have _blubber_ that helps control body temperature.
Nectar is an adaptation to attract _pollinators_ .	Thorny lizards have _channels_ that collect water.

Think Like a Scientist

Math in Science

Graphing Data

What Did You Find Out?

1. Why do scientists use different kinds of graphs to organize data?

Scientists use the kind of graph that best shows their data.

2. Which kind of graph would you use to show how the height of a seedling changes over a month? Why?

Possible answer: _I would use a line graph because it makes it easy to see changes over time._

Think Like a Scientist continued

Graph Data

Seeds and Flowers

Flower	Number of Seeds
1	100
2	400
3	800
4	500

1. Make a pictograph of the data. Write a title at the top. Make a row for each flower.
2. Decide what symbol you will use and how many seeds one symbol will stand for. Make a key.
3. Draw the correct number of symbols in each row.

Number of Seeds

Flower 1	◇
Flower 2	◇◇◇◇
Flower 3	◇◇◇◇◇◇◇◇
Flower 4	◇◇◇◇◇
Key: ◇ = 100 seeds	

Guided Inquiry

Investigate Temperature and Coverings

Question How does a covering affect the temperature when a thermometer is placed in very cold water?

Make a Hypothesis

How will the covering affect the temperature of the thermometer?

Possible answer: If I cover one thermometer with material and keep one thermometer uncovered, then the covered thermometer will stay warmer than the uncovered thermometer.

Identify and Control Variables

Which variable will you change?
I will cover only one thermometer.

Which variable will you observe or measure?
I will observe the temperature of both thermometers.

Which variables will you keep the same?
I will place both thermometers in plastic bags. I will use the same type of thermometer in each bag. I will use the same amount and temperature of water in each cup.

Guided Inquiry continued

Predict

What will happen to the temperature of each thermometer?
The temperature of the thermometer without the covering will be lower than the thermometer with the covering.

Record

Write what you observe in the table below. Record which type of material you used to cover the thermometer.

Temperature Change in Thermometers

Time	Temperature of Thermometer without Covering	Temperature of Thermometer Covered with _____
Start		
1 minute		
2 minutes		
3 minutes		
4 minutes	Temperatures will vary, but students should observe that the temperature of the covered thermometer was higher than the temperature of the uncovered thermometer.	
5 minutes		
6 minutes		
7 minutes		
8 minutes		
9 minutes		
10 minutes		

Guided Inquiry continued

Explain and Conclude

1. Compare the temperatures of the two thermometers. Was your hypothesis supported? Explain.

   Answers will vary based on student hypotheses, but generally students should find that the covered thermometers stayed warmer than the uncovered thermometers.

2. Share your results with other groups. What type of covering kept the thermometers the warmest?

   Answers will vary depending on how thoroughly students cover the thermometers, but generally fake fur and cotton balls will keep the thermometers warmer than feathers.

Guided Inquiry continued

3. Use the results of your experiment to infer how body coverings help animals live in cold temperatures.

   Possible answer: Body coverings such as fur and feathers help animals stay warm in cold temperatures.

Think of Another Question

What else would you like to find out about how coverings affect temperature? How could you find an answer to this new question?

Answers will vary. Record students' questions for possible future investigations.

Name _____ Date _____

SCIENCE
notebook

Directed Inquiry

Investigate Temperature and Cricket Behavior

Question How does temperature affect cricket behavior?

Predict

How will the cooler temperature affect the crickets' behavior?

Predictions may vary. Students may predict that the crickets will slow down

because of the cooler temperature.

Record

Write your observations in the table below.

Cricket Activity

Where Habitat Was	Temperature (°C)	Observations
Classroom		Temperatures will vary. Student observations will vary, but generally they should notice that the crickets are more sluggish after having been in the cooler temperature of the refrigerator.
Refrigerator (after 10 minutes)		
Room temperature (after 5 minutes)		

Name _____ Date _____

SCIENCE
notebook

Directed Inquiry continued

Explain and Conclude

1. Share your results with the class. Did your results support your predictions? Explain.

   Answers will vary, but students may have predicted that the crickets

   would move more slowly in cooler temperatures.

2. How did the change in temperature affect the crickets' behavior?

   After being in cooler temperatures, the crickets moved very

   slowly or did not move at all.

Name _____ Date _____

SCIENCE
notebook

Directed Inquiry continued

3. When the temperature of its environment gets cooler, the processes in a cricket's body slow down. Infer how this might affect a cricket's ability to move and survive.

   Answers will vary, but students may infer that slower body processes

   cause crickets to move more slowly. If the temperature is too cold, the

   crickets could die. Eggs that adult crickets lay in fall can survive and

   hatch in spring.

Think of Another Question

What else would you like to find out about how temperature affects crickets' behavior? How can you find an answer to this new question?

Answers will vary. Record students' questions for possible future

investigations.

Name _____ Date _____

SCIENCE
notebook

Chapter 5 Science Vocabulary

Write one of the vocabulary words in each blank to complete the sentence.

| deciduous |
| evergreen |
| hibernate |
| migrate |
| season |

1. A chipmunk will ___hibernate___ , or sleep deeply, during the winter.

2. A pine tree is a(n) ___evergreen___ because it keeps its leaves during the year.

3. Many geese ___migrate___ to warm places in the fall.

4. A(n) ___season___ is a time of year with certain patterns of weather.

5. A maple tree is ___deciduous___ because it sheds its leaves in the fall.

Write a caption and add labels to the drawing. Use vocabulary words.

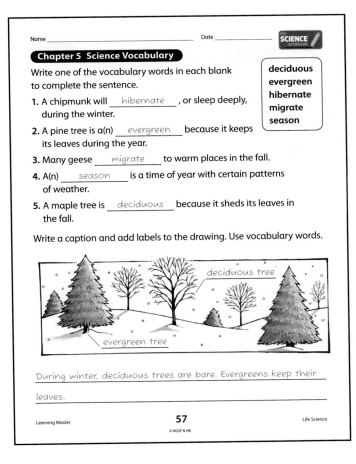

deciduous tree

evergreen tree

During winter, deciduous trees are bare. Evergreens keep their
leaves.

Chapter 5 Share and Compare

Complete each sentence to show how plants and animals respond to cold winters. Use the words and phrases in the box.

> change color
> grow thick coats
> hibernate
> keep leaves
> migrate
> shed leaves
> store food in bulbs

Plants		Animals	
Deciduous trees	_shed leaves_ .	Musk oxen	_grow thick coats_ .
Evergreens	_keep leaves_ .	Arctic foxes	_change color_ .
Lillies, daffodils, and onions _store food in bulbs_ .		Chipmunks	_hibernate_ .
		Monarch butterflies	_migrate_ .

Guided Inquiry

Investigate Temperature and Seed Sprouting

Question How does temperature affect seed sprouting?

Make a Hypothesis

How will the temperature affect seed sprouting? Write your hypothesis.

Possible answer: If I place two seeds in places with different temperatures, then the seeds in the warmer temperature will sprout more quickly.

Identify, Manipulate, and Control Variables

Which variable will you change?
I will change the temperature where the seeds are placed.

Which variable will you observe or measure?
I will observe when the seeds sprout.

Which variables will you keep the same?
I will keep the amount of water and light that the seeds get the same.

Guided Inquiry continued

Record

Write and draw what you observe in the table below.

Temperature and Seed Sprouting

Day	Observations	
	Bag 1: _____ °C	Bag 2: _____ °C
Start: After 30 minutes		
1	Temperatures and observations will vary, but students should observe that seeds at room temperature sprouted more quickly than seeds in the cold temperature.	
3		
5		

Guided Inquiry continued

Explain and Conclude

1. Which seed had grown more by the end of the week?

   Answers will vary, but seeds in the refrigerator generally will grow less than seeds at room temperature. Seeds in the freezer probably will not sprout.

2. What can you conclude about temperature and how seeds sprout?

   Possible answer: I conclude that seeds do not sprout in cold temperatures as quickly as they do at room temperature.

Name _____ Date _____

3. How might seed growth be affected in places that have cold winters?

In places with cold winters, seeds may not sprout until

temperatures become warmer in spring or summer.

_____

_____

_____

Think of Another Question

What else would you like to find out about temperature and seed sprouting? How could you find an answer to this new question?

Answers will vary. Record students' questions for possible future

investigations.

_____

_____

_____

Name _____ Date _____

Do Your Own Investigation

Possible student answers are for the Sample Question and Steps.

Open Inquiry Checklist

☑ Choose a question or make up one of your own.

How do light and darkness affect how seeds sprout

and grow?

☑ Gather the materials you will use.

2 cups with soil

tape

6 sunflower seeds

spoon

cup with water

_____

☑ If needed, make a hypothesis or a prediction.

Possible answer: _If I plant the seeds in light and dark, then the_

seeds in the light will grow into green plants, and the seeds

in the dark will grow into pale plants.

Name _____ Date _____

☑ If needed, identify, manipulate, and control variables.

Variable I will change: _I will change the amount of light the cups_

will get. **Variable I will measure or observe:** _I will observe the color_

of the plants. **Variable I will keep the same:** _I will keep the amount_

of water, type and amount of soil, and temperature the same.

☑ Make a plan for your investigation.

1. _Label 1 cup with soil_ **Light**_. Label the other cup with_

   soil **Dark**_._

2. _Observe the sunflower seeds, and then plant them in the_

   soil with the spoon.

3. _Use the spoon to water the seeds. Give each cup 2_

   spoonfuls of water each day.

4. _Put the Light cup in a sunny place. Put the Dark cup in a_

   dark place with the same temperature as the Light cup.

   Observe the cups each day for 2 weeks, and record

   your observations.

Name _____ Date _____

☑ Carry out your plan.

☑ Collect and record data. Analyze your data.

	Light Cup	Dark Cup
Day 1		
Day 2		
Day 3		
Day 4		
Day 5		
Day 6		
Day 7		
Day 8		
Day 9		
Day 10		
Day 11		
Day 12		
Day 13		
Day 14		

Student observations will vary, but should reflect that while both cups' seeds sprout and grow, the **Light** plants are greener.

Open Inquiry continued

☑ Explain and share your results.

Possible answer: Both seeds sprouted at about the same time, but the **Light** seeds grew into green plants while the **Dark** plants looked pale.

☑ Tell what you conclude.

Possible answer: Seeds don't need light to sprout, but they do need light to grow into green plants.

☑ Think of another question.

Possible answer: How can you grow plants without soil?

Think Like a Scientist

How Scientists Work

Using Models to Study Systems

What Did You Find Out?

1. What is a system?

A system is a group of parts that work together.

2. What are three kinds of models scientists might use to study an ecosystem?

Diagrams, maps, physical models

Think Like a Scientist continued

Plan a Model

1. What question are you trying to answer?

Answers may vary. Possible answer: How does salt water affect the pond?

2. What kind of model or models would you use?

Answers may vary. Possible answer: A physical model of the pond

---

Think Like a Scientist continued

3. Write a procedure for using the model to answer the question.

Answers may vary. Students should provide a clear description of their steps for using the model to answer their question.

4. After talking with others, what changes might you make to your plan?

Answers may vary. Students should present their plan, discuss their plan, and listen to others' feedback before choosing the changes they will make to their plan.

Panel 1 (page 79)

Explore Activity

Investigate Moon Phases

Question How can you model the way the moon's shape seems to change?

Record

Observe the Calendar of Moon Phases. Is there any pattern to the way the moon looks? Describe the pattern you see.

Possible answer: In the beginning of the Calendar, the moon looks totally dark. The moon seems to slowly get lighter from right to left until it is all lit. Then the moon seems to slowly get darker from right to left until it is all dark again.

Panel 2 (page 80)

Explore Activity continued

Draw how the moon's shape appears to change.

Changes in the Moon's Shape in One Month

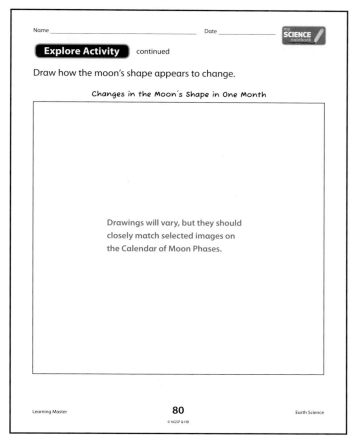

Drawings will vary, but they should closely match selected images on the Calendar of Moon Phases.

Panel 3 (page 81)

Explore Activity continued

Explain and Conclude

1. What pattern do you see in your model of moon phases?

   Possible answer: I see different amounts of the lighted part of the moon. At first the moon is dark. Then the moon begins to be lighted on the right. I see more and more of the moon until the full moon. After the full moon, the right side of the moon begins to appear dark. Then I see less and less of the lighted part of the moon.

2. Describe how your model shows the phases of the moon.

   Possible answer: My model shows what some different phases look like in the proper order as the lighted part of the moon appears to change shape over time.

Panel 4 (page 82)

Explore Activity continued

3. Suppose you are able to see the whole moon in the night sky. Use your model to predict how the shape of the lighted part of the moon will change over the next week.

   Answers will vary, but students should predict they will see less of the lighted part of the moon over the next week.

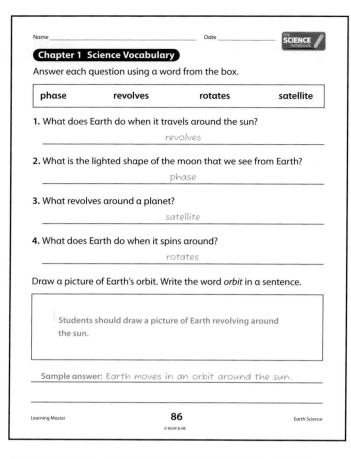

Answer each question using a word from the box.

phase	revolves	rotates	satellite

1. What does Earth do when it travels around the sun?

revolves

2. What is the lighted shape of the moon that we see from Earth?

phase

3. What revolves around a planet?

satellite

4. What does Earth do when it spins around?

rotates

Draw a picture of Earth's orbit. Write the word *orbit* in a sentence.

Students should draw a picture of Earth revolving around the sun.

Sample answer: Earth moves in an orbit around the sun.

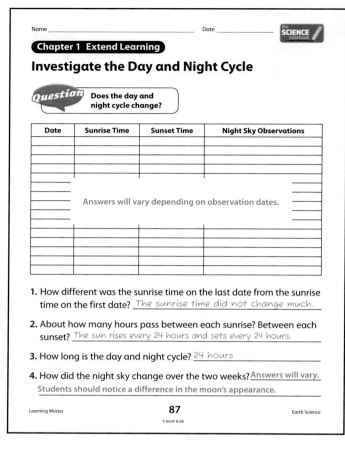

Investigate the Day and Night Cycle

Question Does the day and night cycle change?

Date	Sunrise Time	Sunset Time	Night Sky Observations
	Answers will vary depending on observation dates.		

1. How different was the sunrise time on the last date from the sunrise time on the first date? The sunrise time did not change much.

2. About how many hours pass between each sunrise? Between each sunset? The sun rises every 24 hours and sets every 24 hours.

3. How long is the day and night cycle? 24 hours

4. How did the night sky change over the two weeks? Answers will vary. Students should notice a difference in the moon's appearance.

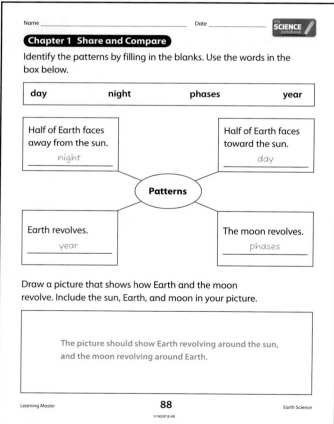

Identify the patterns by filling in the blanks. Use the words in the box below.

day	night	phases	year

Half of Earth faces away from the sun.
night

Half of Earth faces toward the sun.
day

Patterns

Earth revolves.
year

The moon revolves.
phases

Draw a picture that shows how Earth and the moon revolve. Include the sun, Earth, and moon in your picture.

The picture should show Earth revolving around the sun, and the moon revolving around Earth.

Think Like a Scientist ## Math in Science

Bar Graphs

What Did You Find Out?

1. What kind of data would scientists show on a bar graph?

Scientists would use a bar graph to show data that is not changing over time.

2. How can you tell what the different bars on a graph stand for?

The labels across the bottom of the graph tell what the different bars stand for.

Panel 1 (top left):

Name _____ Date _____

Think Like a Scientist continued

Make and Use a Graph

Look at the data below about the rocks in a particular area.
Then use the data to make a bar graph.

Kind of Rock	How Many Collected
Granite	1
Shale	3
Sandstone	5
Pumice	2

Write a title for your graph. Write numbers and **How Many Collected** on the side of the graph. Write **Kind of Rock** and the name of each rock at the bottom. Draw bars to show how many of each rock were collected.

Title: Titles will vary.

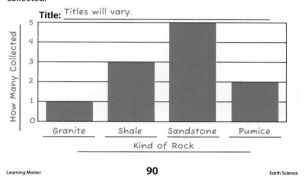

Panel 2 (top right):

Name _____ Date _____

Directed Inquiry

Investigate Sunlight and Shadows

Question How does a shadow caused by sunlight change during the day?

Record

What are your observations of the toy's shadow in step 1?
Answers will vary depending on the time of the day during which this activity takes place. Possible answer: The shadow is the same shape as the toy, but is a little bit slanted.

Write or draw your observations and measurements in the table below.

Changes in Shadows

Date	Time	How High the Sun Looks	Length of Shadow (cm)
Observations and measurements will vary, but students should observe that as the sun appears higher in the sky at midday, the shadows get shorter. As the sun appears lower in the sky in the afternoon, the shadows get longer.			

Panel 3 (bottom left):

Name _____ Date _____

Directed Inquiry continued

Changes in Shadows, continued

Date	Time	How High the Sun Looks	Length of Shadow (cm)
Observations and measurements will vary, but students should observe that as the sun appears higher in the sky at midday, the shadows get shorter. As the sun appears lower in the sky in the afternoon, the shadows get longer.			

Predict

Where will the toy's shadow be 1 hour after your last observation? Write your prediction.
Answers will vary depending on students' predictions.

After 1 hour, does your observation match your prediction? Why or why not?
Answers will vary depending on students' predictions and observations.

Panel 4 (bottom right):

Name _____ Date _____

Directed Inquiry continued

Explain and Conclude

1. Compare your measurements. When was the shadow the shortest and longest? Where was the sun in the sky at those times?
Possible answer: The shadow was shortest around noon when the sun appeared highest in the sky. The shadow was longest early in the morning and late in the afternoon when the sun appeared lower in the sky.

2. What pattern in length and movement did you observe with the shadows?
Possible answer: The shadow got shorter as the morning went by. It was shortest around noon. Then the shadow got longer again during the afternoon. The shadow moved from west to east as the sun appeared to move from east to west.

Panel 1 (page 94)

Directed Inquiry continued

3. What caused the changes you observed in the shadows?

Possible answer: The sun first appeared low in the sky. As the sun appeared to move across the sky, it appeared higher and then lower. This caused the shadows to change position and length.

Think of Another Question

What else would you like to find out about sunlight and shadows? How could you find an answer to this new question?

Answers will vary. Record students' questions for possible future investigations.

Panel 2 (page 95)

Directed Inquiry

Investigate Energy from the Sun

Question What happens to the temperature of water when it is in the sunlight and in the shade?

Record

Write what you observe in the table below.

Water Temperature

Cup	At Start (°C)	After 1 Hour (°C)	After 2 Hours (°C)
Sun		In sunlight — Temperatures will vary, but students should observe that water in the sun has a higher temperature than water in the shade.	In shade
Shade		In shade	In shade

Panel 3 (page 96)

Directed Inquiry continued

Explain and Conclude

1. Compare the temperatures of the water in the 2 cups at the end of 1 hour in step 4.

Possible answer: The temperature of the water in the Sun cup was higher than the temperature of the water in the Shade cup.

2. What happened to the temperature of the water in the Sun cup when it was moved from the sunlight to the shade? Explain why you think this happened.

Possible answer: The temperature went down after we moved the water to the shade. When the cup was moved out of the sunlight, heat was lost.

Panel 4 (page 97)

Directed Inquiry continued

3. Share your data with others. Explain any differences in the data.

Possible answer: Some of the cups may not have been in direct sunlight. Maybe the temperature was written down incorrectly.

Think of Another Question

What else would you like to find out about sunlight and water temperatures? How could you find an answer to this new question?

Answers will vary. Record students' questions for possible future investigations.

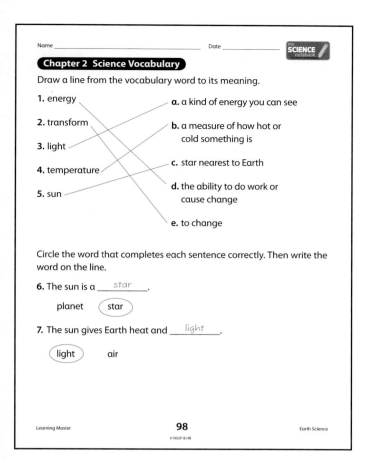

Name _____ **Date** _____

Draw a line from the vocabulary word to its meaning.

1. energy

2. transform

3. light

4. temperature

5. sun

a. a kind of energy you can see

b. a measure of how hot or cold something is

c. star nearest to Earth

d. the ability to do work or cause change

e. to change

Circle the word that completes each sentence correctly. Then write the word on the line.

6. The sun is a ____star____.

   planet   (star)

7. The sun gives Earth heat and ____light____.

   (light)   air

Learning Master   **98**   Earth Science
© NGSP & HB

Name _____ **Date** _____

Chapter 2 Share and Compare

Fill in the lines with the letters identifying the information that is true for each kind of energy.

Food energy _a_ _e_   Solar energy _b_ _d_

Fossil fuels _b_ _c_ _f_   Wind energy _b_ _g_

    a. created by plants now

    b. often used to make electricity

    c. made from plants and animals that lived long ago

    d. collected by solar panels

    e. used, directly or indirectly, by animals

    f. coal, gasoline, and natural gas are types

    g. turns windmills

Write a short paragraph about how people depend on energy from the sun.

Sample answer: Energy from the sun can be used to make electricity. Some forms of energy are fossil fuels, wind energy, and solar energy. These types of energy give us electricity, heat and light our homes and classrooms, and allow us to cook our food. Food energy also comes from the sun. Plants use sunlight to grow, and animals eat plants or other animals that have eaten plants for energy.

Learning Master   **99**   Earth Science
© NGSP & HB

Name _____ **Date** _____

Guided Inquiry

Investigate Sunlight

Question How well do different materials block sunlight?

Make a Hypothesis

Which materials will block sunlight from the light-sensitive beads? Write your hypothesis.

Possible answer: If I place different materials between the sun and light-sensitive beads, then only some of the materials will block the sunlight.

Identify, Manipulate, and Control Variables

Which variable will you change?

I will change the material placed between the sun and the beads.

Which variable will you observe or measure?

I will observe the beads.

Which variables will you keep the same?

I will use the same number of beads and the same size material. I will keep the beads in the same place.

Learning Master   **100**   Earth Science
© NGSP & HB

Name _____ **Date** _____

Guided Inquiry continued

Record

Write what you observe in the table below.

Light-Sensitive Beads

Location	Material Tested	Observation of Beads (no change, slight change, full change)
Shade		no change
Sunlight		full change
Sunlight		
Sunlight		Answers will vary depending on students' choices.

Learning Master   **101**   Earth Science
© NGSP & HB

Guided Inquiry continued

Explain and Conclude

1. Do the results support your hypothesis? Explain.

   Answers will vary depending on student hypotheses.

   _____

   _____

   _____

   _____

2. Compare what happened to the beads in steps 1 and 2. What caused the change in step 2?

   Possible answer: *The color of the beads did not change in*

   step 1, but their color did change in step 2. Sunlight caused

   the change.

   _____

   _____

   _____

Guided Inquiry continued

3. What can you conclude about how well materials block sunlight? What evidence did you use to come to your conclusion?

   Answers will vary, but students might conclude that as the paper, bag

   with sunscreen, and paper towel allowed a small amount of sunlight

   through, the beads turned color slightly. The plastic bag allowed a lot of

   light through, and the beads changed color fully. The foil and wool cloth

   blocked the sunlight and prevented any color change.

Think of Another Question

What else would you like to find out about how to block sunlight? How could you find an answer to this new question?

   Answers will vary. Record students' questions for possible future

   investigations.

   _____

   _____

   _____

Directed Inquiry

Investigate Light Brightness

Question How does a light's brightness appear to change with distance?

Record

Use the Apparent Brightness Scale below to describe brightness. Write what you predict and observe in the table below.

Apparent Brightness Scale	
1	very bright
2	bright
3	dim

Distance and Apparent Brightness of Lights

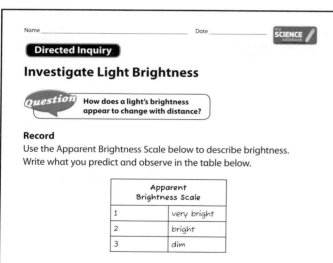

	Penlight	Distance from Observer	Predicted Brightness	Observed Brightness
Start	A	2 m	Predictions and observations may vary. Students may find that the lights have the same apparent brightness when they are the same distance away. Apparent brightness may decrease with distance.	
	B	2 m		
	C	2 m		

Directed Inquiry continued

Distance and Brightness of Lights, continued

	Penlight	Distance from Observer	Predicted Brightness	Observed Brightness
Trial 1	A	2 m		
	B	4 m		
	C	3 m	Predictions and observations will vary. Students should find that the lights have the same apparent brightness when they are the same distance away. Apparent brightness may appear to decrease with distance.	
Trial 2	A	2 m		
	B	3 m		
	C	4 m		
Trial 3	A	2 m		
	B	5 m		
	C	4 m		

Name _____ Date _____ **my SCIENCE notebook**

Directed Inquiry continued

Explain and Conclude

1. Do your results support your predictions? Explain.

   Answers will vary. Students should accurately evaluate how their results

   support their predictions.

   _____

   _____

   _____

   _____

2. What can you conclude about distance and the apparent brightness of lights that are the same size? Use your observations to support your conclusion.

   Possible answer: If two lights are the same size, one light might

   appear less bright if it is farther away than the other light.

   _____

   _____

   _____

Name _____ Date _____ **my SCIENCE notebook**

Directed Inquiry continued

3. Use the results of this investigation to explain how stars that are like each other in size and temperature can appear to have different brightnesses.

   Possible answer: Some stars can be alike in size and

   temperature, but a star that is closer to Earth can

   look brighter than the others.

   _____

   _____

   _____

Think of Another Question

What else would you like to find out about how a light's brightness appears to change with distance? How could you find an answer to this new question?

Answers will vary. Record students' questions for possible future

investigations.

   _____

   _____

   _____

Name _____ Date _____ **my SCIENCE notebook**

Chapter 3 Science Vocabulary

Write one of the words from the box to complete each sentence. You can use the words more than once.

star	property	brightness	telescope

1. Something you can observe about an object, such as its size, is a(n) ___property___ of that object.

2. A(n) ___star___ is a glowing ball of hot gases that can be seen in the night sky.

3. The amount of light an object gives off is called ___brightness___.

4. When you look through a(n) ___telescope___, the things that you look at seem closer and bigger.

5. Color is a(n) ___property___ of stars that gives a clue to how hot they are.

6. A scientist can see more detail by using a(n) ___telescope___ to study the stars.

7. The hottest stars have the greatest ___brightness___ because they give off the most energy for their size.

8. Choose two words from the box and write a sentence about stars that contains both words.

   Sample sentence: One property of a star is its brightness.

Name _____ Date _____ **my SCIENCE notebook**

Chapter 3 Share and Compare

Complete each circle of the web with a property of stars. Choose the property from the box that relates best to the words above or below each circle.

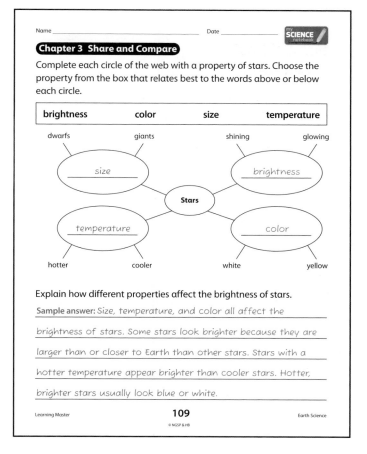

brightness	color	size	temperature

Explain how different properties affect the brightness of stars.

Sample answer: Size, temperature, and color all affect the

brightness of stars. Some stars look brighter because they are

larger than or closer to Earth than other stars. Stars with a

hotter temperature appear brighter than cooler stars. Hotter,

brighter stars usually look blue or white.

Guided Inquiry

Investigate Lenses

Question How can lenses help you see objects that are far away?

Compare

How large did the words look with each lens in step 1?

Students should find that the 200 mm lens magnified the words the most,

and the 100 mm lens magnified the words the least.

_____

_____

_____

_____

Record

What lenses did you choose to make your telescope?

Students should record whether they used the 100, 150, or 200 mm lenses.

_____

_____

Guided Inquiry continued

Record

Write what you observe in the table below.

Observing Stars

	Observations
Without telescope	
With telescope	Observations will vary. Students should be able to see some magnification with the telescope. They may see more magnification when the telescope is reversed, depending on which lenses were placed on the tubes and the order in which they looked through their telescopes.
With telescope reversed	
With another group's telescope	

Guided Inquiry continued

Explain and Conclude

1. How did turning the telescope around affect the stars you observed?

   Answers will vary depending on the lenses used and the order in which

   students looked through their telescopes. Students may be able to see

   the stars by looking through either end of their telescope, but they will

   have to adjust the length of the tube. Students may be better able to view

   more stars by looking through one end of the telescope.

   _____

2. Compare the number of stars you could observe with your telescope and without a telescope.

   Possible answer: I could see more stars with the telescope than

   without it.

   _____

   _____

   _____

Guided Inquiry continued

3. Use your observations to explain how lenses can help scientists study stars.

   Possible answer: Lenses in a telescope allow scientists to

   observe many more stars than they could without using

   a telescope.

   _____

   _____

   _____

Think of Another Question

What else would you like to find out about how lenses can help you see objects that are far away? How could you find an answer to this new question?

Answers will vary. Record students' questions for possible future

investigations.

_____

_____

_____

Directed Inquiry

Investigate Rock Layers

Question How can you model and compare rock layers?

Record

Write or draw in the table below.

Rock Model

Layer	Materials Used	Observations
Bottom	plaster of Paris, water, sand, green food coloring	Observations will vary.
Middle	plaster of Paris, water, pebbles, red food coloring	
Top	plaster of Paris, water, blue food coloring	

Directed Inquiry continued

Explain and Conclude

1. Compare the layers of your model.

   Possible answer: The bottom layer was green and rough like sand. The middle layer was red and bumpy. The top layer was blue and smooth.

2. Compare your model rock to those of other students. Why do you think the models look different?

   Possible answer: Groups might have stirred the mixtures more or less than other groups.

Directed Inquiry continued

3. How is your model rock like the real rocks in the picture on page 111? How is it different?

   Possible answer: My model rock is made of layers that have different properties. Real sedimentary rocks are also made of layers with different properties. My rock is made of plaster of Paris and food coloring. Real rocks are not made of these materials.

Think of Another Question

What else would you like to find out about rock layers? How could you find an answer to this new question?

Answers will vary. Record students' questions for possible future investigations.

Chapter 4 Science Vocabulary

Answer each question using a word from the box.

grain	humus	mineral	soil

1. What is composed of bits of decayed plants and animals? humus

2. What is a solid, nonliving material found in nature? mineral

3. What is the word for a small part of a rock or soil? grain

4. What material from Earth is made up of bits of rocks, decayed matter, air, and water? soil

Draw a picture of two minerals from this chapter.

> Drawing will vary, but should include physical properties such as color and grain size.

Write sentences describing the properties of each mineral you drew.

Answers will vary. Minerals can have several properties, including color, grain size, streak, and hardness.

SCIENCE
notebook

Chapter 4 Extend Learning

Investigate the Ability to Support Plant Growth

Question Which soil type best supports plant growth?

Date	Sandy Soil	Red Clay Soil	Humus Soil
	Answers will vary depending		
	on students' results.		

1. How much did the plants grow in the humus soil after five days? How did this compare with the seeds in the red clay and sandy soil?
   Answers will vary, but the humus soil should show the most growth.

2. How well do each of the soils hold water? How do you think this affects plant growth? Humus soil holds water but drains slowly.
   Red clay absorbs water but does not drain well. Sandy soil
   does not hold water well. Humus soil gives plants the right
   amount of drainage and absorption for them to grow.

SCIENCE
notebook

Chapter 4 Share and Compare

Examine the Venn diagram. Answer the questions below it.

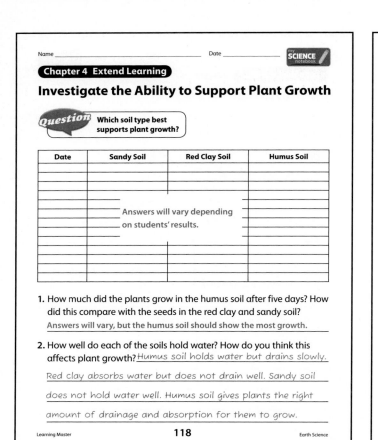

1. What is soil composed of?
   Soil is composed of rock, minerals, and humus.

2. Why do the Minerals and Rocks circles intersect?
   They intersect because minerals are sometimes part of rocks.

3. Why don't the Humus and Rock circles overlap?
   Rocks do not contain humus, and humus does not
   contain rock.

4. Explain what a grain is and give one reason why it is important.
   A grain is a small piece of a rock, mineral, or soil. Presence
   of grains is a property that helps you identify minerals,
   rocks, or soil. Grain size affects how water drains from soil.

SCIENCE
notebook

Guided Inquiry

Investigate Soil and Water

Question Which kind of soil holds the most water?

Make a Hypothesis

Which kind of soil will hold the most water? Write your hypothesis.
Possible answer: If I compare sandy soil, clay soil, and peat,
then I will find that peat holds the most water.

Identify, Manipulate, and Control Variables

Which variable will you change?
I will change the type of soil.

Which variable will you observe or measure?
I will measure the mass of water that stays in the soil after I
water it.

Which variables will you keep the same?
I will use the same amount of soil and water. I will use the same type
of cups and let the water and soil sit for the same amount of time.

SCIENCE
notebook

Guided Inquiry continued

Record

Write what you observe in the table below.

Soil and Water

	Kind of Soil _____	Kind of Soil _____
Observations		
Mass of dry soil and cup (g)	Answers will vary depending on students' choices, but students should find that sandy soil holds the least water, and peat holds the most water.	
Mass of wet soil and cup (g)		
Mass of water in soil (g)		

Name _____ Date _____ my SCIENCE notebook

Guided Inquiry continued

Explain and Conclude

1. Do the results support your hypothesis? Explain.

   Answers will vary depending on student hypotheses.

2. Compare your results with other groups. Which kind of soil holds the most water?

   Answers will vary depending on students' results. Possible answer:

   The peat held the most water because it is light and

   absorbent. The sandy soil held the least amount of water

   because it is not absorbent.

Name _____ Date _____ my SCIENCE notebook

Guided Inquiry continued

3. Infer why soils that hold a medium amount of water would be good for growing plants.

   Possible answer: Soil that holds water would be good for

   growing plants because it would give plants the continual

   supply of water that they need to live. But if the soil holds

   too much water, the plants would not survive.

Think of Another Question

What else would you like to find out about soil and water? How could you find an answer to this new question?

Answers will vary. Record students' questions for possible future

investigations.

Name _____ Date _____ my SCIENCE notebook

Directed Inquiry

Investigate Natural Resources

Question How can you identify and classify natural resources?

Record

Write your observations and classifications in the table below.

Resource Uses and Classification

Resource	Uses	Renewable or Nonrenewable?
Rubber	Answers will vary, but students should include as many uses as possible for each resource.	renewable
Wood		renewable
Metal		nonrenewable

Name _____ Date _____ my SCIENCE notebook

Directed Inquiry continued

Resource Uses and Classification, continued

Resource	Uses	Renewable or Nonrenewable?
Rock	Answers will vary, but students should include as many uses as possible for each resource.	nonrenewable
Soil		nonrenewable
Water		renewable
Air		renewable
Plastic		nonrenewable

Directed Inquiry continued

Use your data to make a graph that shows the number of renewable and nonrenewable resources you found.

Types of Resources

Number of Resources (y-axis: 0–10)

Graphs should reflect the data in students' data tables.

Renewable | Nonrenewable
Resources

Directed Inquiry continued

Explain and Conclude

1. Which resource has the most uses? Is this resource renewable or nonrenewable?

   Possible answer: I found the most uses for wood. Wood is a renewable resource.

2. Compare your data table with the class. Did you classify resources the same? What might you add to your table?

   Possible answer: Yes, my classmates classified the resources the same way I did. I need to add soil as a nonrenewable resource.

Directed Inquiry continued

3. Look at the nonrenewable resources you found. How might you use fewer of these resources every day?

   Answers will vary, but could include ideas like using fewer beverage cans.

Think of Another Question

What else would you like to find out about natural resources? How could you find an answer to this new question?

Answers will vary. Record students' questions for possible future investigations.

Chapter 5 Science Vocabulary

Write one of the words or phrases from the box in each blank to complete the sentence.

| fossil fuel | nonrenewable resources | natural resources |
| recycling | renewable resources | |

1. Sunlight and air are ___renewable resources___ .

2. ___Nonrenewable resources___ include metal and rocks.

3. Living and nonliving things found on Earth that people need are ___natural resources___ .

4. A nonrenewable resource that was formed from the remains of plants and animals is called ___fossil fuel___ .

5. Using an old object to make a new object is ___recycling___ .

Write a caption describing the natural resources in this drawing. Use the terms *renewable resources* and *nonrenewable resources*.

Renewable resources include water, trees, air, and sunlight. Nonrenewable resources include rocks and the fossil fuel from which the backpacks were made.

Name _____ Date _____

Chapter 5 Share and Compare

1. Define *renewable resources* and *nonrenewable resources*.

2. List three renewable resources and three nonrenewable resources.

3. Choose one resource. Write a paragraph describing the resource, how we use it, and how we can care for it.

Earth's Natural Resources	
Renewable Resources	**Nonrenewable Resources**
1. Definition: Renewable resources are resources that will not run out if used wisely.	**1. Definition:** Nonrenewable resources are resources that cannot be replaced quickly enough to keep them from running out.
2. sunlight	**2.** metals
air	rocks
fresh water or plants	fossil fuels (coal, oil, natural gas)

3. Paragraph:

Possible answer: Oil is a nonrenewable resource found underground. We use oil to make plastic and gasoline. We can reduce our need for plastic by drinking from a refillable bottle. We can use less gasoline by walking, biking, or riding a bus.

Name _____ Date _____

Guided Inquiry

Investigate Wind Energy

Question How can you use wind energy to move objects?

Record

Write your data in the table below.

Model Windmill

Number of Spoons	Number of Pennies Lifted

Answers will vary depending on students' choices. Students should find that models with more spoons can lift more pennies.

Name _____ Date _____

Guided Inquiry continued

Explain and Conclude

1. Compare your data with your classmates. How did the number of spoons affect the test?

Students should notice that the more spoons they used, the more pennies the windmill could lift.

2. Describe how the energy from your blowing lifted the objects in the cup.

Possible answer: The energy from my blowing moved the spoons around in a circle, which caused the string to wind around the straw and lifted the cup.

Name _____ Date _____

Guided Inquiry continued

Think of Another Question

What else would you like to find out about wind energy? How could you find an answer to this new question?

Answers will vary. Record students' questions for possible future investigations.

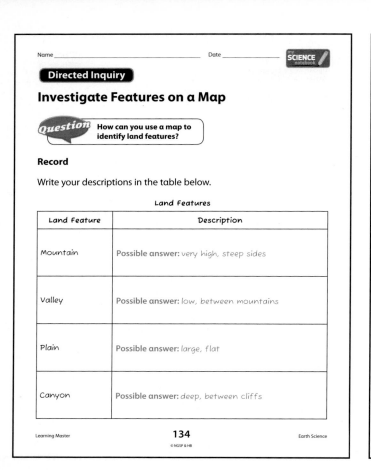

Panel 1 (page 134)

Name _____ Date _____

Directed Inquiry

Investigate Features on a Map

Question How can you use a map to identify land features?

Record

Write your descriptions in the table below.

Land Features

Land Feature	Description
Mountain	**Possible answer:** very high, steep sides
Valley	**Possible answer:** low, between mountains
Plain	**Possible answer:** large, flat
Canyon	**Possible answer:** deep, between cliffs

Panel 2 (page 135)

Name _____ Date _____

Directed Inquiry continued

Land Features, continued

Land Feature	Description
River	**Possible answer:** long, flowing
Lake	**Possible answer:** wide, large body of water

Explain and Conclude

1. How is the Land Features Map different from the Land Features Diagram?

   Possible answer: The map does not show the actual shape of the land feature. The diagram does show the shape.

Panel 3 (page 136)

Name _____ Date _____

Directed Inquiry continued

2. Compare the different land features on the map. How does the map help you identify land features?

   Possible answer: The map helps me identify land features because the map uses shading to show different surfaces. The map key uses color to highlight the different features.

3. Do you think the land features formed slowly or quickly? Explain.

   Answers will vary, but students should say that the land features have formed slowly and then support their answer.

Panel 4 (page 137)

Name _____ Date _____

Directed Inquiry continued

Think of Another Question

What else would you like to find out about maps? How could you find an answer to this new question?

Answers will vary. Record students' questions for possible future investigations.

Directed Inquiry continued

Land Features Diagram

Label these features on the diagram: Mountain, Canyon, Valley, Plain, River, and Lake.

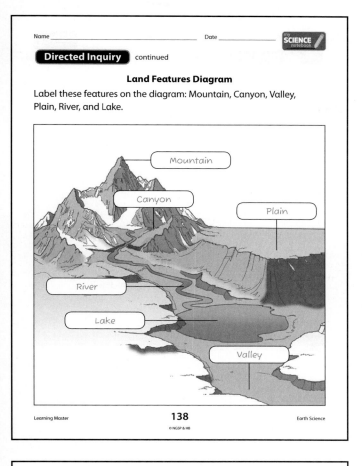

Chapter 6 Science Vocabulary

Write one of the words from the box in each blank to complete the sentence.

deposition	erosion	glacier	landform	weathering

1. A(n) _____glacier_____ moves slowly, picking up soil and rock.

2. A plateau is a(n) _____landform_____ that has a flat top.

3. A beach may form by _____deposition_____ of sand.

4. _____Weathering_____ breaks large rocks into small ones.

5. Rivers form valleys by _____erosion_____ of rocks and soil.

6. The picture below shows large rocks. In the empty box next to the picture, draw what the rocks might look like after weathering happens for many years. Then on the lines below the boxes, write a sentence describing what happens to rocks as they weather.

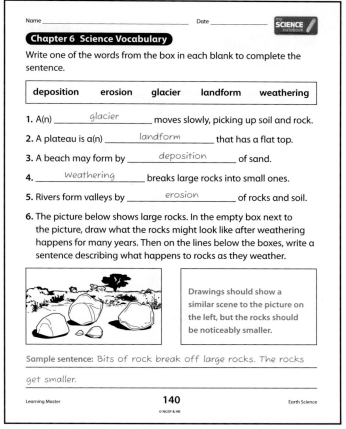

Drawings should show a similar scene to the picture on the left, but the rocks should be noticeably smaller.

Sample sentence: Bits of rock break off large rocks. The rocks get smaller.

Chapter 6 Extend Learning

Investigate How Wind Changes Land

Question How did the wind change the land?

In the boxes below, draw the sand dunes you observed in each pan.

Pan A

Drawings should accurately depict students' observations.

Pan B

1. How were the sand dunes in Pan A different from Pan B?

   Possible answer: The sand dunes in Pan A were larger.

2. Explain why the objects in Pan B made the sand dunes different.

   Possible answer: The objects blocked the wind from the dryer and changed how the wind moved the sand around.

3. How did changing the speed of the air make the sand dunes different?

   Possible answer: The higher speed blew the sand around more.

4. How did changing the direction of the air make the sand dunes different?

   Possible answer: Changing the direction of the air made the dunes form in the direction the air blew.

Chapter 6 Share and Compare

1. The landforms in the box below were caused mostly by erosion, weathering, or deposition. Fill in the web by writing each word in the correct circle. You may use the words more than once.

valley	canyon	sand dune	Devil's Tower	beach

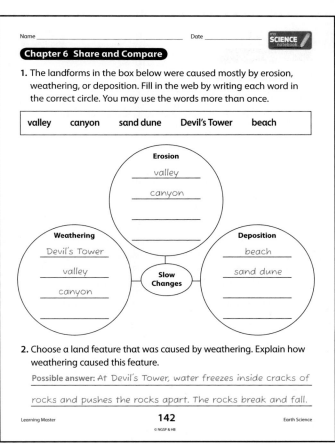

Erosion
valley
canyon

Weathering
Devil's Tower
valley
canyon

Slow Changes

Deposition
beach
sand dune

2. Choose a land feature that was caused by weathering. Explain how weathering caused this feature.

   Possible answer: At Devil's Tower, water freezes inside cracks of rocks and pushes the rocks apart. The rocks break and fall.

Guided Inquiry

Investigate Glaciers

Question How can you make a model to show what happens when glaciers move?

Predict

What will happen when the model glacier flows over soil, sand, and rocks? Write your prediction.

The model glacier will move some soil, sand, and rock as

it flows.

_____

_____

_____

_____

_____

Guided Inquiry continued

Record

Write and draw your observations in the table below.

Glacier Model Observations

What I Observed	What Happened
Model of Earth's features without glacier	Observations and drawings will vary, but students should draw before and after pictures of their model of Earth's land. In their after drawings, students should show that the glacier model moved some sand, soil, and rock as it flowed.
Model of Earth's features with glacier	

Guided Inquiry continued

Explain and Conclude

1. Did your results support your prediction? Explain.

Answers will vary depending on students' predictions and results.

_____

_____

_____

_____

_____

2. Compare your results with those of other groups. Did the glacier flow the same way in other models? What might cause differences?

Answers will vary, but students could cite differences in mixture

consistency and orientation of model Earth features as sources for

differing results, such as moving rocks and sand.

_____

_____

_____

Guided Inquiry continued

3. How is your model like a real glacier? How is it different?

Possible answer: Alike: Glaciers move downhill and change

Earth's features. Different: The model glacier moved

much faster than a real glacier and is made up of

different substances.

_____

_____

Think of Another Question

What else would you like to find out about glaciers? How could you find an answer to this new question?

Answers will vary. Record students' questions for possible future

investigations.

_____

_____

_____

_____

Page 147

Name _____ Date _____

my SCIENCE notebook

Directed Inquiry

Investigate Plate Movements

Question **What are ways Earth's plates can move?**

Record

Write and draw your observations in the table below.

Model Plate Movements

Movement	Observations
← →	Students should observe the mixture ooze up in the space between the hardboard pieces.
→ ←	Students should observe the hardboard piece sinking and the foam piece sliding over the top of it.
↑ ↓	Students should observe the foam pieces sliding past each other.

Learning Master **147**
© NGSP & HB
Earth Science

Page 148

Name _____ Date _____

my SCIENCE notebook

Directed Inquiry continued

Explain and Conclude

1. Describe three ways Earth's plates can move.

   Earth's plates can move toward each other, away from each other, or in opposite directions beside each other.

2. The melted rock under Earth's surface is very hot. What do you think would happen to real melted rock below Earth's surface if the Earth's plates moved apart as the model plates did in step 3?

   Possible answer: Real melted rock would move up to Earth's surface. It would then cool and harden into rock.

Learning Master **148**
© NGSP & HB
Earth Science

Page 149

Name _____ Date _____

my SCIENCE notebook

Directed Inquiry continued

3. What happened to the plates when you moved them together in step 4? How do you think Earth's surface changes when real plates move together?

   Possible answer: One plate moved on top of the other. When real plates move together, some of Earth's surface moves up to form hills or mountains.

Think of Another Question

What else would you like to find out about plate movements? How could you find an answer to this new question?

Answers will vary. Record students' questions for possible future investigations.

Learning Master **149**
© NGSP & HB
Earth Science

Page 150

Name _____ Date _____

my SCIENCE notebook

Chapter 7 Science Vocabulary

Circle the word that completes each sentence correctly. Then write the word on the line.

1. A(n) _____plate_____ is a piece of Earth's crust that slowly moves.
   (plate)   magma

2. _____Magma_____ is melted rock below Earth's surface.
   (Magma)   Lava

3. _____Earthquakes_____ are a shaking of the ground.
   (Earthquakes)   Volcanoes

4. Melted rock above Earth's surface is called _____lava_____.
   (lava)   a plate

5. A(n) _____volcano_____ is an opening in Earth's crust.
   plate   (volcano)

Draw a volcano. Label the lava and magma.

Students should draw lava on the outside of their volcano. They should also label magma on the inside of the volcano.

Write a sentence using *earthquake* and *plates*.

Sample answer: An earthquake can happen when plates move.

Learning Master **150**
© NGSP & HB
Earth Science

Learning Master

273

Answer Key

© NGSP & HB

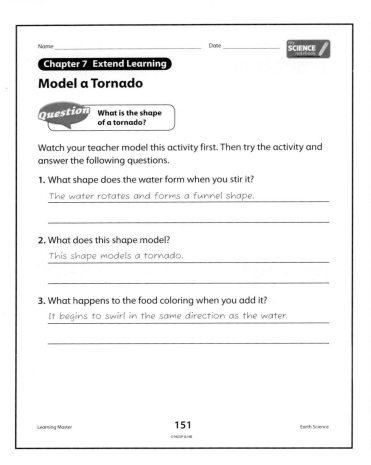
Chapter 7 Extend Learning

Model a Tornado

Question What is the shape of a tornado?

Watch your teacher model this activity first. Then try the activity and answer the following questions.

1. What shape does the water form when you stir it?

   The water rotates and forms a funnel shape.

2. What does this shape model?

   This shape models a tornado.

3. What happens to the food coloring when you add it?

   It begins to swirl in the same direction as the water.

Learning Master   **151**   Earth Science
© NGSP & HB

 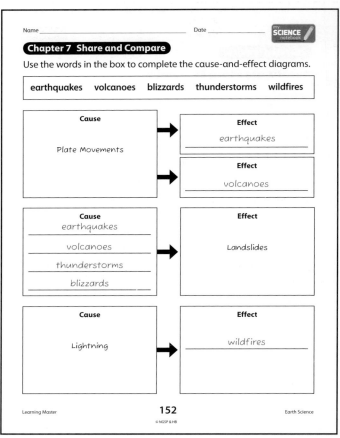
Chapter 7 Share and Compare

Use the words in the box to complete the cause-and-effect diagrams.

| earthquakes | volcanoes | blizzards | thunderstorms | wildfires |

Cause		**Effect**
Plate Movements	→	*earthquakes*
	→	**Effect** *volcanoes*

Cause		**Effect**
earthquakes *volcanoes* *thunderstorms* *blizzards*	→	Landslides

Cause		**Effect**
Lightning	→	*wildfires*

Learning Master   **152**   Earth Science
© NGSP & HB

 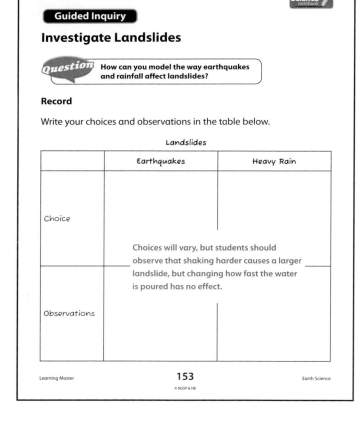
Guided Inquiry

Investigate Landslides

Question How can you model the way earthquakes and rainfall affect landslides?

Record

Write your choices and observations in the table below.

Landslides

	Earthquakes	Heavy Rain
Choice		
Observations	Choices will vary, but students should observe that shaking harder causes a larger landslide, but changing how fast the water is poured has no effect.	

Learning Master   **153**   Earth Science
© NGSP & HB

Guided Inquiry continued

Explain and Conclude

1. How did the force of the shaking and the speed of the pouring affect the landslides?

   Possible answer: *Shaking harder caused a larger landslide than shaking gently. Pouring quickly or slowly had little effect on the landslide.*

2. Use the results of this investigation to infer what can cause real landslides to happen.

   Landslides are likely to happen after a lot of rain falls or when earthquakes happen.

Learning Master   **154**   Earth Science
© NGSP & HB

Name_____ Date_____

Guided Inquiry continued

Think of Another Question

What else would you like to find out about landslides? How could you find an answer to this new question?

Answers will vary. Record students' questions for possible future

investigations.

_____

_____

_____

_____

Name_____ Date_____

Directed Inquiry

Investigate Condensation

Question How can you observe condensation and frost?

Record

Write and draw your observations in the table below.

Metal Cans

Can	After 2 Minutes		After 3 More Minutes	
	Temperature (°C)	Observations	Temperature (°C)	Observations
Ice and salt				
Ice and water				

Measurements and observations will vary, but students should observe that the Ice and Salt can was colder than the Ice and Water can and had frost instead of liquid water on the outside of it.

Name_____ Date_____

Directed Inquiry continued

Explain and Conclude

1. Look for patterns in your data. What do you think caused the condensation on the cans?

   Possible answer: The water vapor in the air got colder and

   turned to liquid water and frost when it touched the cans.

   _____

   _____

   _____

2. Compare your observations of the 2 cans. Which can formed water on the outside faster? Which can formed frost? What do you think caused the differences?

   The outside of the Ice and Water can did not have

   anything on it after 2 minutes, but the Ice and Salt can had

   some frost on it. After 3 more minutes, the Ice and Water

   can had some liquid water on the outside of it. The

   Ice and Salt can had more frost. The lower temperature of

   the Salt and Ice can caused frost to form.

Name_____ Date_____

Directed Inquiry continued

3. How does this investigation model what happens in the water cycle?

   During the water cycle, water vapor in the air changes to

   liquid water when the temperature gets colder. Frost can

   form when water vapor comes in contact with an object

   that is colder than the freezing point of water.

   _____

   _____

Think of Another Question

What else would you like to find out about condensation? How could you find an answer to this new question?

Answers will vary. Record students' questions for possible future

investigations.

_____

_____

_____

_____

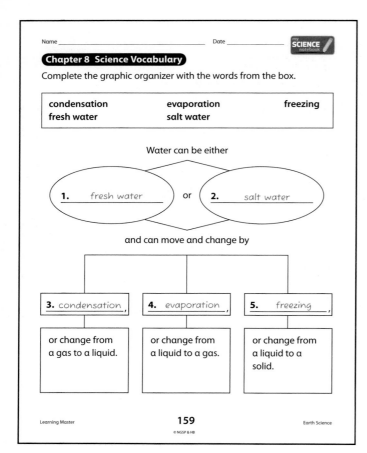

Complete the graphic organizer with the words from the box.

condensation	evaporation	freezing
fresh water	salt water	

Water can be either

1. fresh water   or   **2.** salt water

and can move and change by

3. condensation, | **4.** evaporation | **5.** freezing,
or change from a gas to a liquid. | or change from a liquid to a gas. | or change from a liquid to a solid.

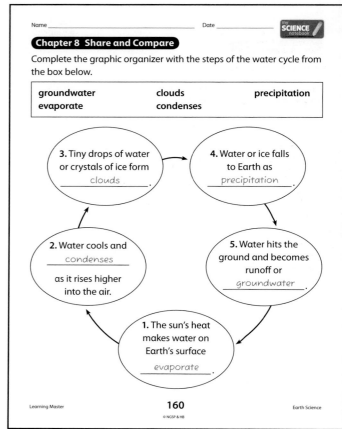

Complete the graphic organizer with the steps of the water cycle from the box below.

groundwater	clouds	precipitation
evaporate	condenses	

3. Tiny drops of water or crystals of ice form _clouds_.

4. Water or ice falls to Earth as _precipitation_.

2. Water cools and _condenses_ as it rises higher into the air.

5. Water hits the ground and becomes runoff or _groundwater_.

1. The sun's heat makes water on Earth's surface _evaporate_.

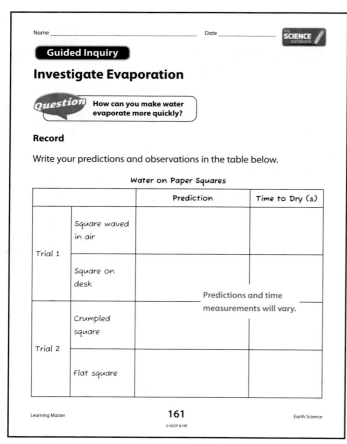

Investigate Evaporation

Question How can you make water evaporate more quickly?

Record

Write your predictions and observations in the table below.

Water on Paper Squares

		Prediction	Time to Dry (s)
Trial 1	Square waved in air		
	Square on desk		
Trial 2	Crumpled square	Predictions and time measurements will vary.	
	Flat square		

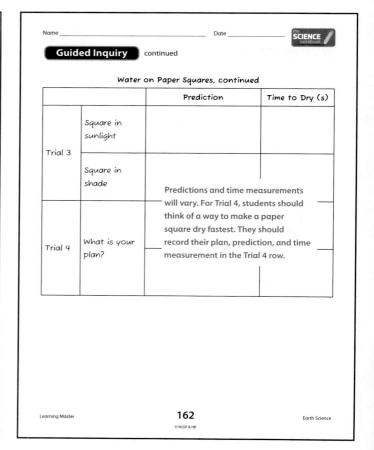

Water on Paper Squares, continued

		Prediction	Time to Dry (s)
Trial 3	Square in sunlight		
	Square in shade		
Trial 4	What is your plan?	Predictions and time measurements will vary. For Trial 4, students should think of a way to make a paper square dry fastest. They should record their plan, prediction, and time measurement in the Trial 4 row.	

Guided Inquiry continued

Explain and Conclude

1. What can you conclude about what makes water evaporate more quickly?

Possible answer: _The water evaporated more quickly from the_
square that I waved back and forth and the square that
was in the sun. When I crumpled the square, it dried at
about the same rate as the square that I did not crumple. I
conclude that moving air and sunlight make water
evaporate more quickly.

2. Compare your data from step 6 with the data from other groups. What did you do to your paper to make it dry more quickly? What did the group with the fastest drying time do?

Answers will vary depending on students' results.

Guided Inquiry continued

3. Use your observations to infer whether water from a lake would evaporate more quickly on a windy day or a calm day. Where would the water from the lake go?

Possible answer: _The moving air on a windy day would cause_
the water in the lake to evaporate more quickly. The water
would go into the air in the form of water vapor.

Think of Another Question

What else would you like to find out about evaporation? How could you find an answer to this new question?

Answers will vary. Record students' questions for possible future
investigations.

Open Inquiry

Do Your Own Investigation

Open Inquiry Checklist

Possible student answers are for the Sample Question and Steps.

☑ Choose a question or make up one of your own.

How do the colors in sunlight compare to the colors in light
from a flashlight?

☑ Gather the materials you will use.

white paper

prism

flashlight

☑ If needed, make a hypothesis or a prediction.

Possible answer: _If I let light from the sun and light from a_
flashlight shine through a prism, then I won't see the same
number of colors.

Open Inquiry continued

☑ If needed, identify, manipulate, and control variables.

Variable I will change: _I will change the source of light that shines_
through the prism. **Variable I will measure or observe:** _I will observe_
the colors of light that form on the other side of the prism.
Variables I will keep the same: _I will keep the prism the same. I will_
keep the paper the same.

☑ Make a plan for your investigation.

1. _Put the white paper in a very sunny place. Place the prism_
   upright on the end of the paper closest to the sun.
2. _Slowly twist and turn the prism until a band of colored_
   light is visible. Observe and record the visible colors.
3. _Move the paper to a darkened area. Place the prism in the_
   center of the paper.
4. _Shine a flashlight on the prism. Move the flashlight until a_
   band of colors is visible. Observe and record the visible
   colors.

Open Inquiry continued

☑ Carry out your plan.
☑ Collect and record data. Analyze your data.

Light Through a Prism

Light Source	Observation
Sun	**Possible answer:** The light spread out and formed bands of red, orange, yellow, green, blue, indigo, and violet.
Flashlight	**Possible answer:** The light spread out and formed bands of orange, yellow, blue, indigo, and violet.

Open Inquiry continued

☑ Explain and share your results.

Possible answer: Both the light from the sun and the light from the flashlight spread out when it went through the prism. Both formed bands of colored light. The colors formed by the sun included red, orange, yellow, green, blue, indigo, and violet. The flashlight's bands did not include red or green.

☑ Tell what you conclude.

Possible answer: Light from the sun contains different colors than light from a flashlight.

☑ Think of another question.

Possible answer: How could I merge the bands of color back into one band of white light?

Think Like a Scientist

Science and Technology

Using Solar Energy

What Did You Find Out?

1. What is solar energy?

   Solar energy is energy from the sun.

2. Why is solar energy a good source of energy?

   Solar energy is renewable energy, or energy that will not run out.

3. How is solar energy used?

   Solar energy can be used to make electricity or to heat food and water.

Think Like a Scientist continued

Observe Solar Energy

Answer these questions about the rocks you placed in the sun for 30 minutes. Which rock feels the warmest?

Answers will vary. Students may find that the rock inside the "house" feels warmest, and the rock under the cup feels warmer than the exposed rock.

Explain why you think this is so.

Answers will vary. Students should explain that the rocks felt warm because they absorbed energy from the sun. They may note that the rock inside the "house" felt the warmest because the walls of the house trapped the sun's energy, and heat could not escape. The plastic cup also kept some heat from escaping, though not as much as the "house." The exposed rock felt the coolest because some of the solar energy it absorbed escaped into the surrounding air.

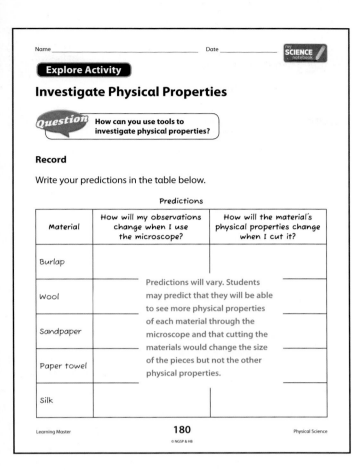

Explore Activity

Investigate Physical Properties

Question How can you use tools to investigate physical properties?

Record

Write your predictions in the table below.

Predictions

Material	How will my observations change when I use the microscope?	How will the material's physical properties change when I cut it?
Burlap		
Wool		Predictions will vary. Students may predict that they will be able to see more physical properties of each material through the microscope and that cutting the materials would change the size of the pieces but not the other physical properties.
Sandpaper		
Paper towel		
Silk		

Explore Activity   continued

Write and draw what you observe in the table below.

Observations of Physical Properties

Material	Before Cutting			After Cutting		
	Just Eyes	Hand Lens	Microscope	Just Eyes	Hand Lens	Microscope
Burlap						
Wool						
Sandpaper		Observations will vary. Students should describe the color, texture, and other physical properties that are visible using just their eyes, the hand lens, and the microscope.				
Paper towel						
Silk						

Explore Activity   continued

Explain and Conclude

1. Did your results support your predictions? Explain.

Answers will vary, depending on students' predictions.

_____

_____

_____

_____

2. How did tools help you to better observe the objects?

Possible answer: I was better able to see that the objects were made of tiny parts.

_____

_____

_____

_____

Explore Activity   continued

3. Compare the physical properties of the large pieces of the materials with the physical properties of the very small pieces.

Possible answer: The size of the pieces changed, but the physical properties of the material did not change.

_____

_____

_____

_____

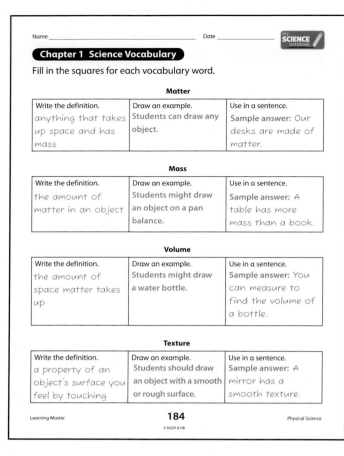

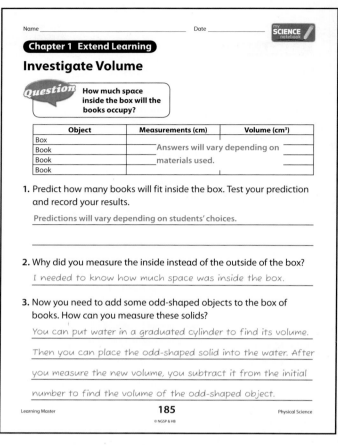

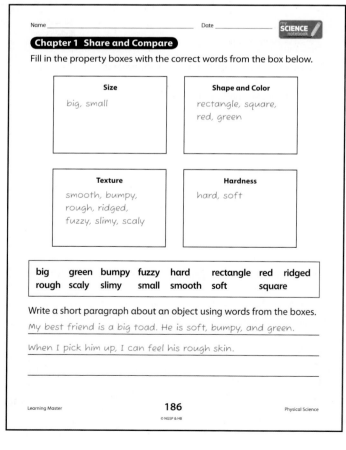

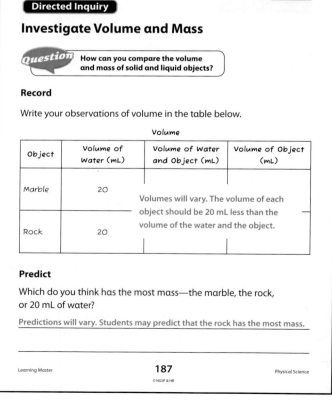

Name _____ Date _____

Directed Inquiry continued

Record

Write your observations of mass in the table below.

Mass

Object	Mass of Cup (g)	Mass of Cup and Object (g)	Mass of Object (g)
Marble			
Rock		Masses will vary. The mass of each object should be the difference between the mass of the cup and object and the mass of the cup.	
Water			

Name _____ Date _____

Directed Inquiry continued

Explain and Conclude

1. Compare the volume of the water, marble, and rock. Which had the most volume?

   Answers will vary depending on the rock that is used. The marble should

   have a volume of about 2 mL.

2. Which object had the most mass? Is that what you predicted? Explain.

   Predictions will depend on the rock that is used.

Name _____ Date _____

Directed Inquiry continued

3. Share your results with others. Explain any differences.

   Answers will vary. Students might state that differences are due to

   incorrect reading of the balance or graduated cylinder, or to differences

   in the actual mass or volume of the objects.

Think of Another Question

What else would you like to find out about comparing the volume and mass of solids and liquids? How could you find an answer to this new question?

Answers will vary. Record students' questions for possible future

investigations.

Name _____ Date _____

Directed Inquiry

Investigate Water and Temperature

Question What happens to water as the temperature changes?

Predict

What will happen to the water in the bags when you put the bags in the freezer in step 2?

Predictions will vary. Students may predict that the water in both bags will

freeze, and its shape will no longer be able to change.

What will happen to the water in the bags when you put the bags in sunlight in step 5?

Predictions will vary. Students may predict that the water in the open Bag 1

will evaporate, but the water in the closed Bag 2 will evaporate and

condense inside the closed bag.

Directed Inquiry continued

Record

Write or draw what you observe in the table below.

Observations of Bags with Water

	Bag 1	Bag 2
After 1 day in the freezer		
After 30 minutes on the desk		
After 1 day in sunlight	Observations will vary. Students should observe that the shape of the ice does not change, but the shape of liquid water does. When the water is in sunlight, it evaporates into air. In the closed bag, the water evaporates and condenses onto the inside of the bag.	
After 2 days in sunlight		
After 3 days in sunlight		

Directed Inquiry continued

Explain and Conclude

1. Did your results support your predictions? Explain.

   Answers will vary, but students may have predicted that the water in both

   bags on the desk would melt, the water in the open bag would evaporate,

   and water in the sealed bag would evaporate and condense on the bag.

   _____

   _____

   _____

2. Compare your results with the results of other groups. What patterns do you see?

   Answers will vary. Students should notice patterns in how the water

   changes in each step.

   _____

   _____

   _____

   _____

Directed Inquiry continued

3. Use your results from steps 2–6 to conclude what happens to water when the temperature goes down. What happens to frozen water when the temperature goes up?

   Possible answer: When the temperature goes down, water

   freezes and becomes solid. When the temperature goes up,

   frozen water melts and becomes liquid. It may evaporate

   and become a gas. In a closed plastic bag, some water may

   evaporate and then condense into a liquid.

   _____

Think of Another Question

What else would you like to find out about what happens to water as the temperature changes? How could you find an answer to this new question?

Answers will vary. Record students' questions for possible future

investigations.

_____

_____

Chapter 2 Science Vocabulary

Write the word that fits each description. Use the words in the box. You will use some words more than once.

states of matter solid liquid gas evaporation condensation

1. Always keeps its shape: ___solid___

2. Gas changes to a liquid: ___condensation___

3. Solid, liquid, gas: ___states of matter___

4. Takes the shape of its container: ___liquid___

5. Liquid changes to a gas: ___evaporation___

6. Spreads out to fill a space: ___gas___

7. Water vapor turns to drops of water: ___condensation___

8. Liquid water turns to water vapor: ___evaporation___

Complete the chart with vocabulary words.

States of Matter	Ways the State of Matter Changes
solid	evaporation
liquid	condensation
gas	

Name _____ Date _____

Chapter 2 Share and Compare

Complete the chart with details from the box below.

Water

States	Properties	Changes to
solid	keeps its shape	a liquid: _melting_
liquid	takes the shape of its container	a solid: _freezing_ a gas: _boiling_ or _evaporation_
gas	spreads to fill a space	a liquid: _condensation_

Details

boiling	gas	solid
condensation	keeps its shape	spreads to fill a space
evaporation	liquid	takes the shape of its container
freezing	melting	

Name _____ Date _____

Think Like a Scientist

Math in Science

Measuring Temperature

What Did You Find Out?

1. What are two reasons why scientists use thermometers to measure temperature?

Scientists can get a more exact temperature measurement with a thermometer. They can measure the temperature of things that are too hot or too cold to touch.

2. What two scales are used to measure temperature? Which do scientists usually use?

Fahrenheit and Celsius; scientists usually use the Celsius scale to measure temperature.

Name _____ Date _____

Think Like a Scientist continued

Measure the Temperature of Water

What was the temperature of the water on both the Fahrenheit and Celsius scales?

Fahrenheit: Answers will vary.

Celsius: Answers will vary.

What was the temperature of the water in your partner's cup on both the Fahrenheit and Celsius scales?

Fahrenheit: Answers will vary.

Celsius: Answers will vary.

How did your temperature readings compare with your partner's readings? What might cause differences between the measurements?

Possible answer: The temperature reading for my cup was slightly higher than my partner's reading. The difference could have been caused by cooling of the water before my partner measured its temperature.

Name _____ Date _____

Guided Inquiry

Investigate Melting

 Question How does heating and cooling affect the properties of different materials?

Make a Hypothesis

What will happen to the temperature and properties of the frozen materials as they sit in sunlight? Write your hypothesis.

Possible answer: If I place the frozen materials in sunlight, then the temperature of the materials will go up and they will melt. The solid materials will change to liquids.

Identify, Manipulate, and Control Variables

Which variable will you change?

I will put different liquids in the cups.

Which variable will you observe or measure?

I will measure the temperature and properties of the liquids.

Which variables will you keep the same?

I will use the same type of cup and the same amount of each liquid. I will place both cups in the freezer and in sunlight for the same amount of time.

Guided Inquiry continued

Record

Write what you observe in the table below.

Liquid in Cups

	Water		My Choice: _____	
	Temperature	Observations	Temperature	Observations
Before freezing				
After freezing				
After 10 min in sunlight				
After 20 min in sunlight				
After 30 min in sunlight				
After 40 min in sunlight				

Answers will vary depending on the choice of liquid. Students should note the temperature and physical properties of each material before freezing, after freezing, and after being placed in sunlight. The amount of time needed for observation will vary. Students may not use all rows on the table, or may need to continue their tables on separate sheets of paper as necessary.

Guided Inquiry continued

Explain and Conclude

1. What happened to the temperature of the liquids in the freezer? What happened to the temperature of the materials in sunlight?

   The temperature of the materials went down in the freezer.

   The temperature of the materials went up in sunlight.

   _____

   _____

   _____

2. How did the properties of the materials change as their temperatures changed? Do these results support your hypothesis? Explain.

   Possible answer: As the temperatures of the water and the juice went down, they began to change from liquids to solids. The materials were solids when they were placed in sunlight, but as their temperatures went up, they began to change to liquids. The results support my hypothesis.

Guided Inquiry continued

3. Compare the results of all groups. What patterns do you observe?

   Possible answer: All the liquids became solids as their temperatures went down. All the materials changed back to liquids as their temperatures went up in the sunlight. Salt water melted fastest. Vinegar melted slowest. Water and juice took about the same amount of time to melt.

Think of Another Question

What else would you like to find out about changes in temperature and properties of materials? How could you find an answer to this new question?

Answers will vary. Record students' questions for possible future investigations.

_____

_____

_____

Directed Inquiry

Investigate Forces and Motion

Question How do forces affect motion?

Record

Write what you observe in the table below.

Motion of Ball

Trial	Prediction (cm)	How Far Ball Moves (cm)
Low ramp on floor		
High ramp on floor	Observations will vary. Students may observe that the ball moves farther after rolling down the high ramp than after rolling down the low ramp and that the ball rolls farther on the floor than on the fabric.	
Low ramp on fabric		
High ramp on fabric		

Page 204

Directed Inquiry continued

Explain and Conclude

1. Did your results support your predictions? Explain.

Answers will vary, but should include mention of the predictions, the

results, and whether the predictions were supported.

_____

_____

_____

_____

2. Compare how the ball moved when you rolled it down the low and the high ramp. What do you think caused the difference?

Possible answer: The ball did not roll as far from the low ramp

as it did from the high ramp. The ball rolled with more force

on the high ramp.

_____

_____

_____

Page 205

Directed Inquiry continued

3. Compare how the ball moved on the floor and on the fabric. What do you think caused the difference?

Possible answer: The ball moved farther on the floor. Friction

from the fabric made the ball move more slowly.

_____

_____

_____

_____

Think of Another Question

What else would you like to find out about forces and motion? How could you find an answer to this new question?

Answers will vary. Record students' questions for possible future

investigations.

_____

_____

_____

Page 206

Chapter 3 Science Vocabulary

Write the word that completes each sentence. Use the words in the box.

| force | friction | gravity | magnetism | motion | speed |

1. When an object is moving, it is in ___motion___.

2. The distance an object moves in a period of time is the object's ___speed___.

3. A push or a pull is a ___force___.

4. A force that acts when two surfaces rub together is ___friction___.

5. A force that pulls an object to the center of Earth is ___gravity___.

6. A force between magnets and the objects magnets attract is ___magnetism___.

7. How are gravity and magnetism alike?

Sample answer: Gravity and magnetism are forces that can pull

objects. Gravity and magnetism do not need to touch an

object to pull it.

8. How are all forces alike?

Sample answer: All forces are pushes or pulls.

Page 207

Chapter 3 Extend Learning

Investigate Changes in Motion

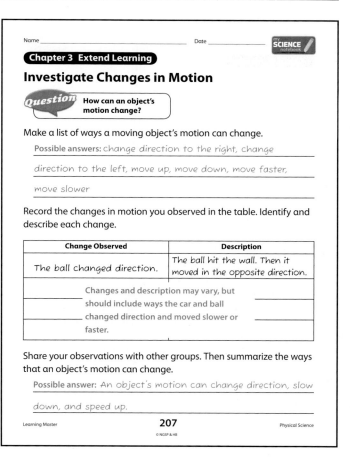

Question How can an object's motion change?

Make a list of ways a moving object's motion can change.

Possible answers: change direction to the right, change

direction to the left, move up, move down, move faster,

move slower

Record the changes in motion you observed in the table. Identify and describe each change.

Change Observed	Description
The ball changed direction.	The ball hit the wall. Then it moved in the opposite direction.
Changes and description may vary, but should include ways the car and ball changed direction and moved slower or faster.	

Share your observations with other groups. Then summarize the ways that an object's motion can change.

Possible answer: An object's motion can change direction, slow

down, and speed up.

Chapter 3 Share and Compare

Classify each word in the box as a force or a change in motion. Then write each word in the table.

direction	friction	gravity	magnetism
position	pull	push	speed

Forces	Changes in Motion
friction, gravity, magnetism, pull, push	direction, position, speed

Compare two forces. How are they alike?
Sample answer: Gravity and magnetism can change the
movement of an object by pulling on it.

Contrast two forces. How are they different?
Sample answer: Friction changes the movement of an object
when objects touch each other. Gravity can change the
movement of an object without touching it.

Choose an object that a force can move. Describe the object's position. Explain what force or forces can cause the object to move or to change its motion.
Sample answer: The paper clip is on top of the table. Magnetism
can move the paper clip by pulling it toward a magnet.

Guided Inquiry

Investigate Motion and Position

Question How can you describe the motion of an object by observing its position?

Record

How will you move the ball from circle A to circle C? Write your plan. Be sure to list the materials you will use and the steps you will take to move the ball.

Plans will vary depending on student choices.
_____
_____
_____
_____
_____
_____
_____

Guided Inquiry   continued

Write your data in the table below.

Path of Ball

Trial	Distance from Circle B (cm)
1	
2	Measurements will vary.
3	

Explain and Conclude

1. How did the ball's position change in relation to circle A? How did it change in relation to circle C?
   Possible answer: The ball moved away from circle A and toward
   circle C.

Guided Inquiry   continued

2. Compare your data. In which trial did the ball come closest to circle B? Describe the path of the ball in that trial. Describe the ball's position in relation to circle B.
   Possible answer: The ball came closest to circle B in trial 2. The
   ball started out from circle A toward circle B. As the ball
   passed circle B, it was 2 cm above it. Then the ball moved
   away from circle B toward circle C.

3. Conclude how you can use position to describe motion.
   Motion can be described by how an object's position
   changes.

Guided Inquiry continued

Think of Another Question

What else would you like to find out about motion and position? How could you find an answer to this new question?

Answers will vary. Record students' questions for possible future

investigations.

_____

_____

_____

Directed Inquiry

Investigate Energy of Motion

Question How does adding more washers affect the motion of a pendulum?

Record

Write what you predict and observe in the table below.

Pendulum Swings

Number of Washers	Prediction	Number of Swings
1		
3	Answers will vary depending on students' predictions and observations.	
5		

Directed Inquiry continued

Use your data to make a bar graph below.

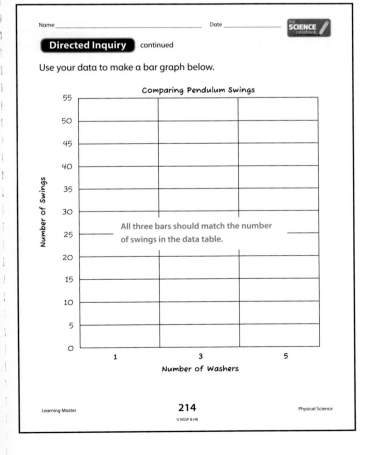

Comparing Pendulum Swings

All three bars should match the number of swings in the data table.

Number of Swings

Number of Washers

Directed Inquiry continued

Explain and Conclude

1. Did your results support your predictions? Explain.

   Possible answer: My predictions were not supported because I predicted that adding washers would result in more swings in one minute.

   _____

   _____

2. Compare the number of swings the pendulum made with 1, 3, and 5 washers. How did increasing the number of washers affect the motion of the pendulum?

   As the number of washers increased, the number of swings did not change.

   _____

   _____

   _____

Name _____ Date _____

Directed Inquiry continued

3. Describe the motion of the pendulum. Where in its swing does the pendulum move fastest? Where does it move slowest?

Possible answer: _The pendulum moves fastest at the very_

bottom of its swing. It moves slowest at the very top of

its swing.

Think of Another Question

What else would you like to find out about how adding more washers can affect the swing of a pendulum? How could you find an answer to this new question?

Answers will vary. Record students' questions for possible future

investigations.

Name _____ Date _____

Chapter 4 Science Vocabulary

Write one of the words from the box in each blank to complete the sentence.

electricity	energy	mechanical energy	heat	sound

1. A car driving down a hill has ____mechanical energy____.

2. An oven bakes food using ____heat____ energy.

3. ____Energy____ is the ability to do work or cause a change.

4. DVD players need ____electricity____ to make them work.

5. When someone talks, we hear ____sound____.

Write a caption for the drawing. Use the words *energy* and *heat*.

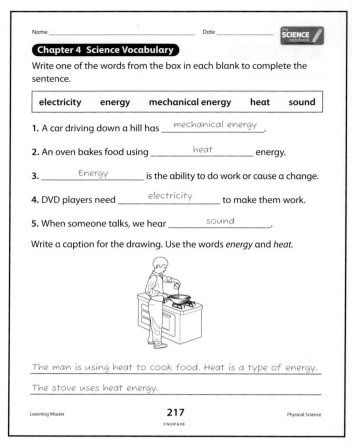

The man is using heat to cook food. Heat is a type of energy.

The stove uses heat energy.

Name _____ Date _____

Chapter 4 Extend Learning

Investigate Mechanical Energy

Question How high will a ball bounce?

Height (Stored Energy)	Prediction (Energy of Motion)	Observation (Energy of Motion)
0.5 m	0.5 m	0.39 (39 cm)
1 m	1 m	0.87 (87 cm)
1.5 m	1.5 m	1.37 (137 cm)

Analyze your data and record your conclusions below.

The higher the ball is before you drop it, the higher it will

bounce after it hits the floor. The more stored energy the ball

has, the more energy of motion it has.

Name _____ Date _____

Chapter 4 Share and Compare

1. Write a definition for energy.

2. List the different types of energy in this chapter.

3. Write what you learned about each type of energy.

4. Write how people use each type of energy.

What Is Energy?		
Energy is the ability to do work or cause a change.		
Type of Energy	**Description**	**How People Use Energy**
mechanical	· stored energy (no movement) · energy of motion (moving object)	· move objects
sound	· energy you can hear · volume—loud or soft · pitch—high or low	· music · communication
electrical	· energy that flows through wires	· use radios, televisions, ovens, vacuum cleaners · read and write at night
heat	· flow of energy from a warmer object to a cooler object	· bake cookies · cook soup

---

Name _____ Date _____

Guided Inquiry

Investigate Vibrations and Sound

Question How does the length of a tuning fork affect the pitch of the sound it makes?

Record

Write what you observe in the table below.

Tuning Forks

Tuning Fork Length (cm)	What Happened to the Salt When You Touched the Tine to the Plastic Wrap?	Did It Make a Sound With a High or Low Pitch?
	Tuning fork lengths will vary. Students may observe that the salt on the plastic wrap moves when the tines of the tuning forks touch the plastic wrap. A shorter tuning fork will make a sound with a higher pitch than a longer tuning fork.	

Name _____ Date _____

Guided Inquiry continued

Explain and Conclude

1. What happened to the salt when you touched the tuning forks to the plastic wrap? Explain why you think this happened.

   The salt moved when I touched the tuning fork to the plastic wrap. I think this happened because the tuning fork made the plastic wrap vibrate and caused the salt to move.

2. Compare the sounds made by the tuning forks. How did the length of the tuning fork affect the pitch of the sound it made?

   The longer tuning fork made a sound with a lower pitch than the shorter tuning fork.

Name _____ Date _____

Guided Inquiry continued

3. When an object vibrates faster, it makes a sound with a higher pitch than an object that is vibrating more slowly. Use your observations to infer which of your tuning forks vibrated faster.

   Possible answer: I infer that the shorter tuning fork vibrated more quickly than the longer tuning fork. The shorter tuning fork made a sound with a higher pitch.

Think of Another Question

What else would you like to find out about vibrations and sound? How could you find an answer to this new question?

Answers will vary. Record students' questions for possible future investigations.

Name _____ Date _____

Directed Inquiry

Investigate Light and Heat

Question What happens to an object's temperature when light shines on it?

Record

Write what you observe and predict in the table below.

Light and Temperature

	Temperature (°C)	Predictions
Start	Temperatures will vary, but students should observe that the temperature increases when the light is on and decreases when the light is off.	What will happen to the temperature if you turn on the lamp?
Light on 5 minutes		What will happen to the temperature if you leave the lamp on for 5 more minutes?

Directed Inquiry continued

Light and Temperature, continued

	Temperature (°C)	Predictions
Light on 10 minutes		What will happen to the temperature if you turn the lamp off?
Light off 5 minutes	Temperatures will vary, but students should observe that the temperature increases when the light is on and decreases when the light is off.	What will happen to the temperature if you leave the lamp off for 5 more minutes?
Light off 10 minutes		

Directed Inquiry continued

Explain and Conclude

1. Did your observations support your predictions? Explain.

Answers will vary, but students may have predicted that the light would

increase the temperature of the thermometer.

_____

_____

_____

2. What happened to the temperature as the lamp shined on the thermometer longer? What happened after you turned off the lamp?

Possible answer: The temperature of the thermometer kept

going up when the lamp was turned on. It kept going down

when the lamp was turned off.

_____

_____

Directed Inquiry continued

3. What can you conclude about what can happen to the temperature of an object when light shines on it?

The temperature of an object goes up when light shines

on it.

_____

_____

_____

Think of Another Question

What else would you like to find out about what happens to an object's temperature when light shines on it? How could you find an answer to this new question?

Answers will vary. Record students' questions for possible future

investigations.

_____

_____

Chapter 5 Science Vocabulary

Write two sentences about each of the words below. The first sentence should be the word's definition. The second sentence should give an example of the word. Share and discuss your sentences with your classmates.

1. light

Possible answer: Light is a kind of energy that we can see.

The sun is our greatest source of natural light.

2. reflection

Possible answer: Reflection is the bouncing of light off of an

object. You can see a clear reflection if you look in a mirror.

3. refraction

Possible answer: Refraction is the bending of light when it

moves through one kind of matter to another kind of matter.

You can see refraction if you put a straw in a glass of water.

4. absorption

Possible answer: Absorption is the taking in of light by a

material. You can feel absorption if you wear a black hat in

the sun.

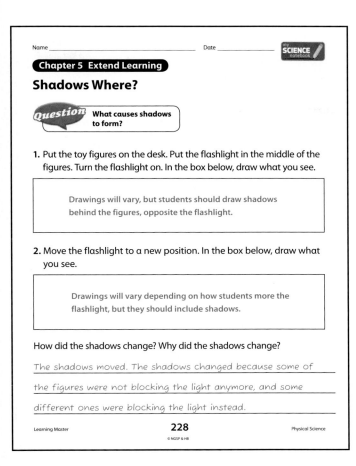

Name _____ Date _____ my SCIENCE notebook

Chapter 5 Extend Learning

Shadows Where?

Question What causes shadows to form?

1. Put the toy figures on the desk. Put the flashlight in the middle of the figures. Turn the flashlight on. In the box below, draw what you see.

> Drawings will vary, but students should draw shadows behind the figures, opposite the flashlight.

2. Move the flashlight to a new position. In the box below, draw what you see.

> Drawings will vary depending on how students more the flashlight, but they should include shadows.

How did the shadows change? Why did the shadows change?

The shadows moved. The shadows changed because some of
the figures were not blocking the light anymore, and some
different ones were blocking the light instead.

Learning Master **228** Physical Science
© NGSP & HB

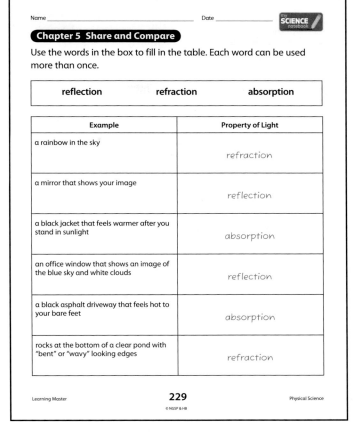

Name _____ Date _____ my SCIENCE notebook

Chapter 5 Share and Compare

Use the words in the box to fill in the table. Each word can be used more than once.

reflection	refraction	absorption

Example	Property of Light
a rainbow in the sky	refraction
a mirror that shows your image	reflection
a black jacket that feels warmer after you stand in sunlight	absorption
an office window that shows an image of the blue sky and white clouds	reflection
a black asphalt driveway that feels hot to your bare feet	absorption
rocks at the bottom of a clear pond with "bent" or "wavy" looking edges	refraction

Learning Master **229** Physical Science
© NGSP & HB

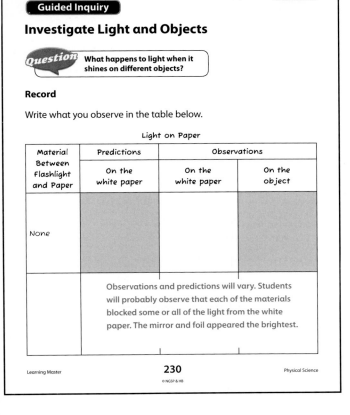

Name _____ Date _____ my SCIENCE notebook

Guided Inquiry

Investigate Light and Objects

Question What happens to light when it shines on different objects?

Record

Write what you observe in the table below.

Light on Paper

Material Between Flashlight and Paper	Predictions	Observations	
	On the white paper	On the white paper	On the object
None			
		Observations and predictions will vary. Students will probably observe that each of the materials blocked some or all of the light from the white paper. The mirror and foil appeared the brightest.	

Learning Master **230** Physical Science
© NGSP & HB

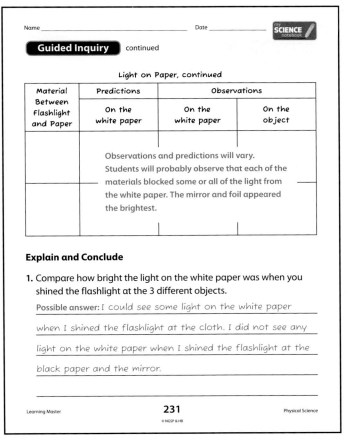

Name _____ Date _____ my SCIENCE notebook

Guided Inquiry continued

Light on Paper, continued

Material Between Flashlight and Paper	Predictions	Observations	
	On the white paper	On the white paper	On the object
		Observations and predictions will vary. Students will probably observe that each of the materials blocked some or all of the light from the white paper. The mirror and foil appeared the brightest.	

Explain and Conclude

1. Compare how bright the light on the white paper was when you shined the flashlight at the 3 different objects.

Possible answer: _I could see some light on the white paper_
when I shined the flashlight at the cloth. I did not see any
light on the white paper when I shined the flashlight at the
black paper and the mirror.

Learning Master **231** Physical Science
© NGSP & HB

Guided Inquiry continued

2. Were you able to see the same amount of light on all 3 objects in step 5? Why do you think that is so?

Possible answer: I could see some light on the black paper and the cloth, but I could see the most light on the mirror and the foil. Some of the light was absorbed by the cloth and the black paper. Some light could pass through the cloth. Most of the light bounced off the mirror and the foil.

3. Based on the results of your investigation, what can you infer about what happens to light when it shines on different objects?

Possible answer: Shiny objects reflect the most light. Other objects may reflect some light, absorb some light, or let some light pass through.

Guided Inquiry continued

Think of Another Question

What else would you like to find out about what happens to light when it shines on different objects? How could you find an answer to this new question?

Answers will vary. Record students' questions for possible future investigations.

Open Inquiry

Do Your Own Investigation

Open Inquiry Checklist

Possible student answers are for the Sample Question and Steps.

☑ Choose a question or make up one of your own.

How can you make water evaporate more quickly?

☑ Gather the materials you will use.

petri dish

tape

graduated cylinder

water

marker

fan

☑ If needed, make a hypothesis or a prediction.

Possible answer: If I allow 2 dishes of water to sit overnight, and 1 of the dishes has a fan blowing on it, then more water will evaporate from the dish with a fan blowing on it.

Open Inquiry continued

☑ If needed, identify, manipulate, and control variables.

Variable I will change: I will change whether air blows onto the water. Variable I will measure or observe: I will observe the level of water in each dish. Variables I will keep the same: I will keep the amount and temperature of water I start with in each dish the same. I will keep the location of both dishes the same.

☑ Make a plan for your investigation.

1. Label half of the petri dish **Fan**. Label the other half **No Fan**.

2. Measure and pour 30 mL of water in each dish.

3. Observe the level of the water. Use tape and a marker to mark the water level in each dish.

4. Place both dishes in a sunny place. Place the fan so that it blows onto the water in the **Fan** dish only.

5. The next day, observe and compare the level of water in the dishes.

Name _____ Date _____ SCIENCE notebook

Open Inquiry continued

☑ Carry out your plan.

☑ Collect and record data. Analyze your data.

Evaporation of Water

	No Fan	Fan
Observations of water level at the start of the investigation	Possible answer: The water is at the 30 mL level where I placed the tape.	Possible answer: The water is at the 30 mL level where I placed the tape.
Observations of the water level the next day	Possible answer: The water level is about three-fourths the height of the tape.	Possible answer: The water level is very low. Almost all of the water evaporated.

Name _____ Date _____ SCIENCE notebook

Open Inquiry continued

☑ Explain and share your results.

Possible answer: _The level of water that had air blowing on it_ _was lower than the level of water that did not have air_ _blowing on it._

☑ Tell what you conclude.

Possible answer: _The water that had air blowing on it_ _evaporated faster. Air blowing across the surface of water_ _made the water evaporate faster._

☑ Think of another question.

Possible answer: _What effect does the speed of air blowing_ _across the water have on how fast the water evaporates?_

Name _____ Date _____ SCIENCE notebook

Think Like a Scientist **How Scientists Work**

Using Observations to Evaluate Explanations

What Did You Find Out?

1. What are three ways that scientists might organize their data?

   Scientists might organize their data as a written description, _as a drawing or photograph, or in numbers._

2. Why do scientists analyze their data?

   Scientists analyze their data to find out whether the data _support their ideas and explanations._

Name _____ Date _____ SCIENCE notebook

Think Like a Scientist continued

Evaluate Explanations

Rico's data are shown in the table below. Analyze the data, and then answer the question.

Mass of Water Balloons

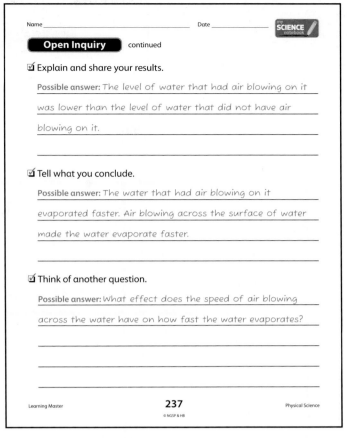

Trial	Mass of Large Balloon	Mass of Small Balloon
1	615 g	246 g
2	615 g	246 g
3	615 g	246 g

Do you agree with Rico's idea that the bigger water balloon has more mass? Write a paragraph explaining your answer. Be sure to use Rico's data to support your argument.

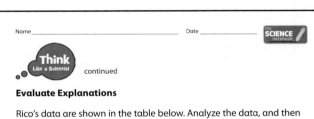

Possible answer: _I agree with Rico's idea that the large_ _water balloon has more mass because its mass is 615 g, and_ _the mass of the small balloon is only 246 g. I think that Rico's_ _data are correct because he measured each balloon several_ _times to be sure he did not make a mistake._

K-W-L Chart

K What Do I Know	W What Do I Want To Learn?	L What Did I Learn?

© NGSP & HB

Word Web

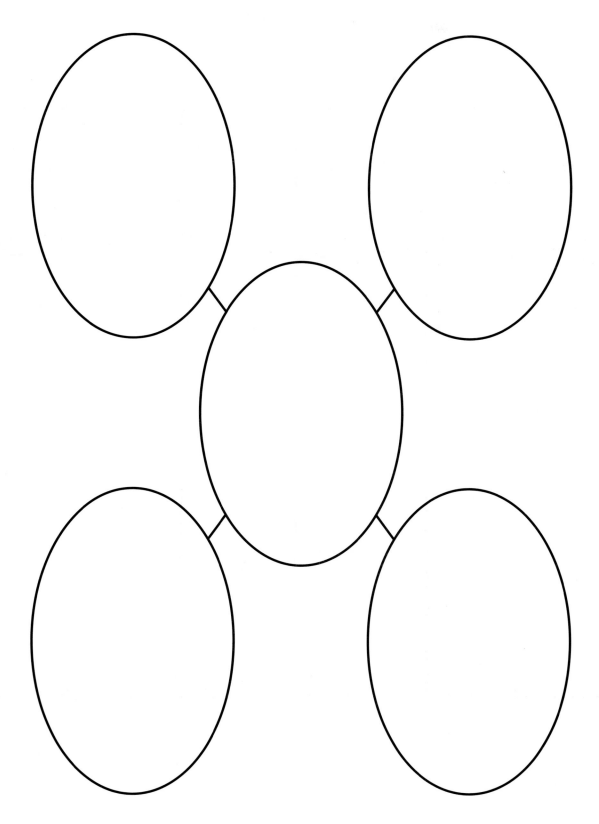

Vocabulary Cards

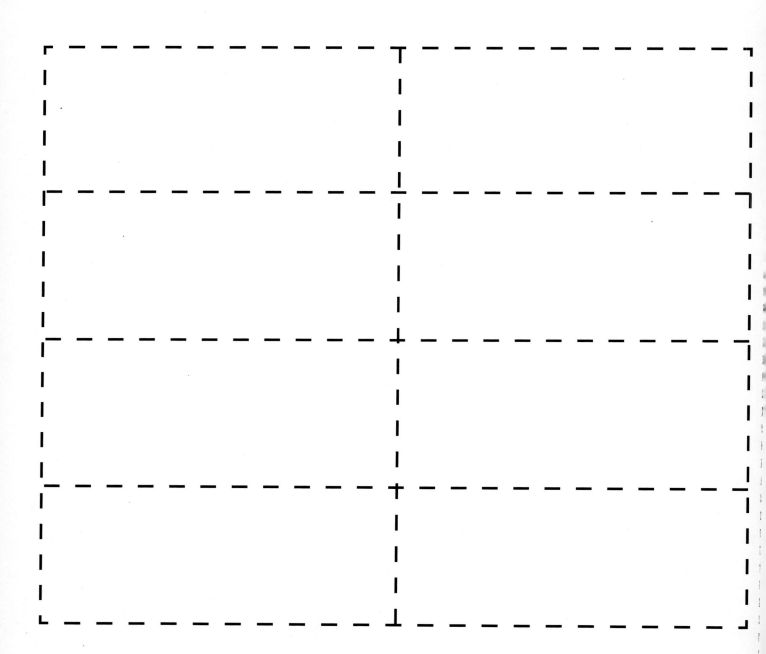

© NGSP & HB

T-Chart

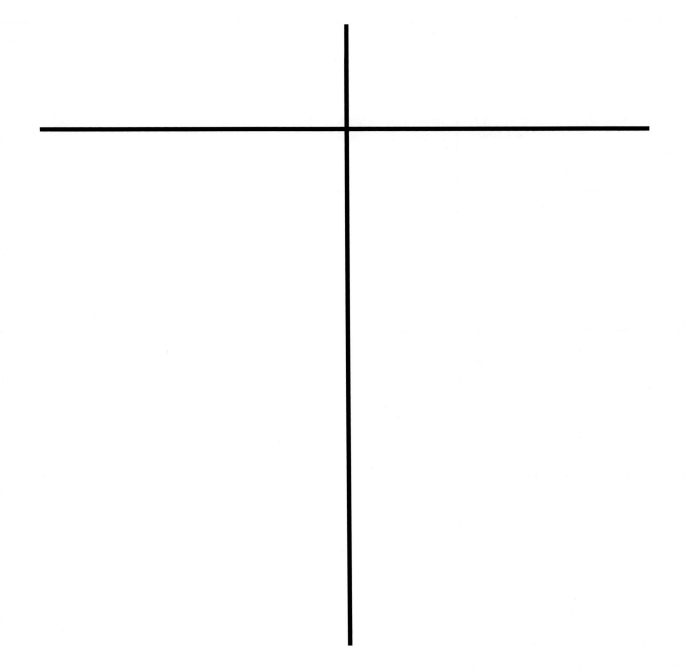

© NGSP & HB

Three-Column Chart

© NGSP & HB

Compare and Contrast

Alike   Different

Venn Diagram

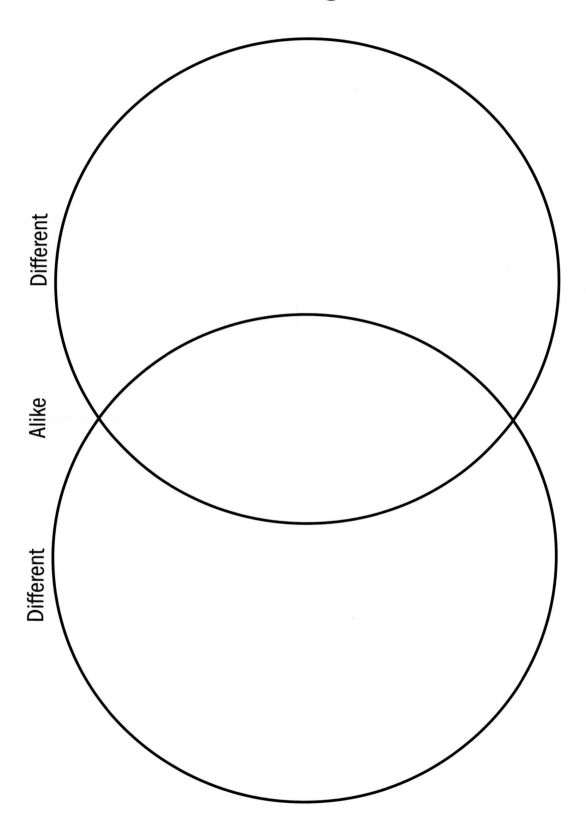

Different

Alike

Different

© NGSP & HB

Sorting Chart

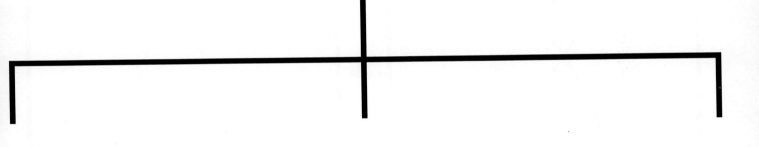

© NGSP & HB

Predict

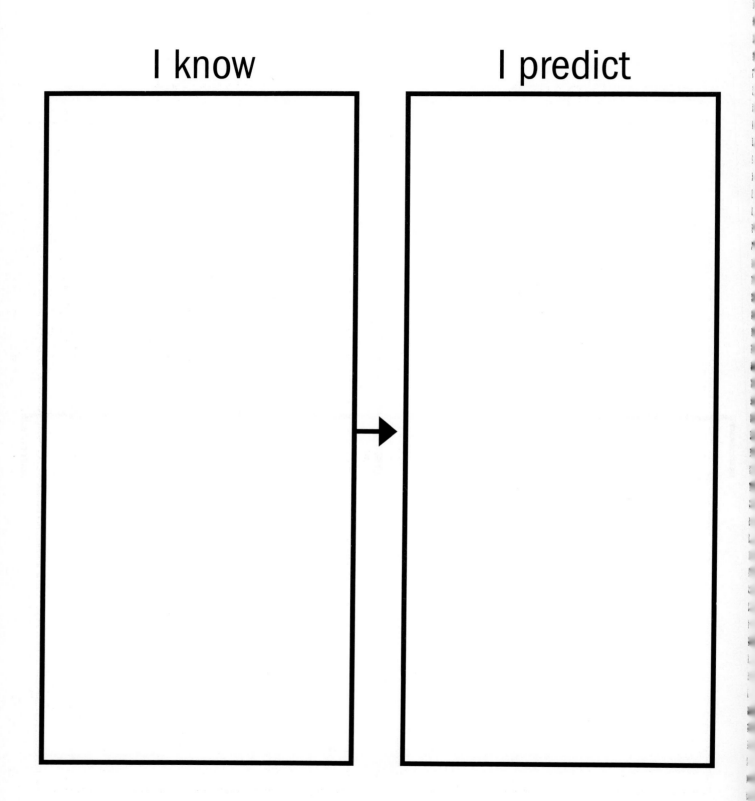

I know

I predict

© NGSP & HB

Cause-and-Effect Chart

Cause

Effect

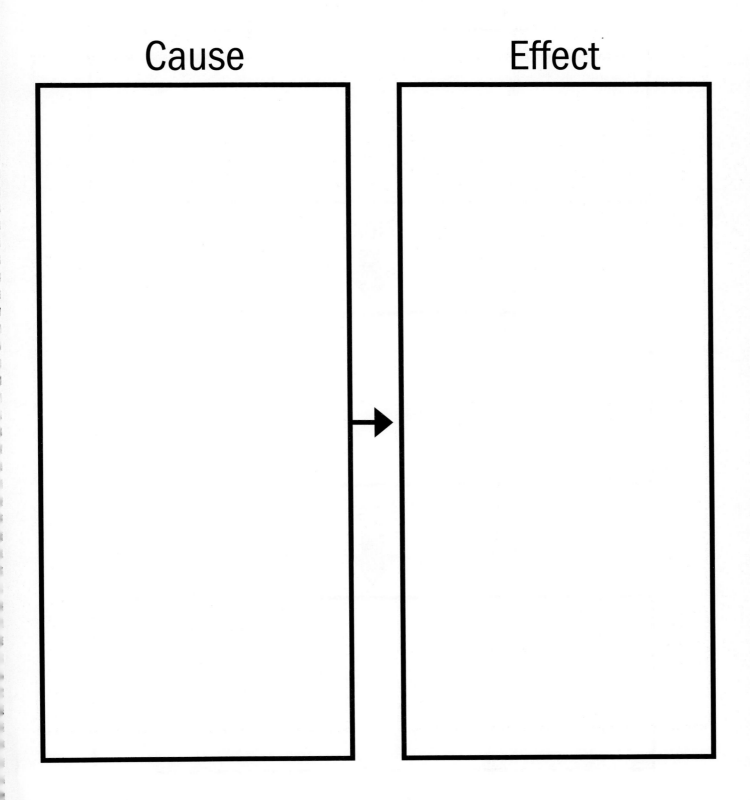

Put Things in Order

First

Next

Last

© NGSP & HB

Make Inferences

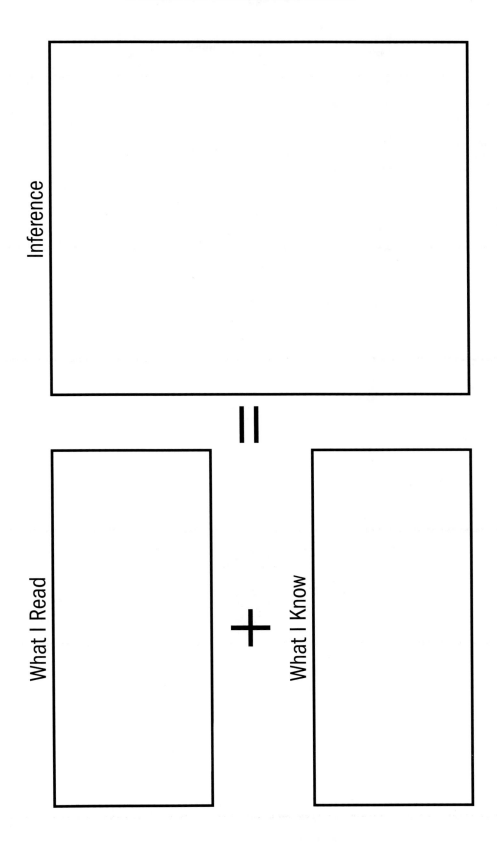

Inference

What I Read

+

What I Know

© NGSP & HB

Credits

Acknowledgments
Grateful acknowledgment is given to the authors, artists, photographers, museums, publishers, and agents for permission to reprint copyrighted material. Every effort has been made to secure the appropriate permission. If any omissions have been made or if corrections are required, please contact the Publisher.

Photographic Credits
Front Cover Image Mark Thiessen/National Geographic Image Collection. **83** William Radcliffe/Science Faction/Corbis. **84-85** David Scheuber/Shutterstock. All other photos by Andrew Northrup.

Illustrator Credits
All illustrations by Ruth Flanigan and Paul Dolan.

Neither the Publisher nor the authors shall be liable for any damage that may be caused or sustained or result from conducting any of the activities in this publication without specifically following instructions, undertaking the activities without proper supervision, or failing to comply with the cautions contained herein.

Program Authors
Randy Bell, Ph.D., Associate Professor of Science Education, University of Virginia, Charlottesville, Virginia; Malcolm B. Butler, Ph.D., Associate Professor of Science Education, University of South Florida, St. Petersburg, Florida; Kathy Cabe Trundle, Ph.D., Associate Professor of Early Childhood Science Education, The Ohio State University, Columbus, Ohio; Judith Sweeney Lederman, Ph.D., Director of Teacher Education and Associate Professor of Science Education, Department of Mathematics and Science Education, Illinois Institute of Technology, Chicago, Illinois; David W. Moore, Ph.D., Professor of Education, College of Teacher Education and Leadership, Arizona State University, Tempe, Arizona

The National Geographic Society
John M. Fahey, Jr., President & Chief Executive Officer
Gilbert M. Grosvenor, Chairman of the Board

Copyright © 2011 The Hampton-Brown Company, Inc., a wholly owned subsidiary of the National Geographic Society, publishing under the imprints National Geographic School Publishing and Hampton-Brown.

All rights reserved. No part of this book may be reproduced or transmitted in any form or by any means, electronic or mechanical, including photocopying, recording, or by an information storage and retrieval system, without permission in writing from the Publisher.

National Geographic and the Yellow Border are registered trademarks of the National Geographic Society.

National Geographic School Publishing
Hampton-Brown
www.NGSP.com

Printed in the USA.
RR Donnelley, Menasha, WI.

ISBN: 978-0-7362-7741-9

10 11 12 13 14 15 16 17 18 19

10 9 8 7 6 5 4 3 2 1